Measurement: Grade 4

S0-AKN-866

Table of Contents

Measurement: Grade 4

Introduction

Teachers are well aware of the importance of developing strong mathematics skills in their students. Students, on the other hand, may not understand how math will be a useful tool outside of school. That is why application of math skills, once mastered, to real-life situations is vital to students' appreciation of math.

Mathematics skills are used in almost every aspect of our lives, from an early age. Students may not realize that they are using math skills when they build, draw, cook, or score a game. By showing them that these skills do relate to math, teachers and parents can help students make the connection.

Measurement is one of the most common ways that students will use mathematics, both as students and as adults. From dressing for the weather to coming home on time or spending allowances, students estimate and use measurement skills throughout their day.

The National Council for Teachers of Mathematics has set standards for mathematical content and the processes through which students should gain and use their knowledge. Measurement is one of the five content areas set forth in the standards. In the fourth grade, students should use a variety of tools and techniques to measure, apply the results in problem-solving situations, and communicate the reasoning used in solving these problems. This book provides opportunities for learning measurement concepts in accordance with the NCTM standards.

Organization

Measurement is divided into eight units covering estimation, length, capacity, temperature, mass, time, money, and computation. Each unit provides opportunities for hands-on learning, as well as applications to real-life situations. Students use estimation skills and then prove their measurements. Part of each unit is devoted to metric measurements. Tools needed for hands-on activities are listed at the bottom of the page.

Each unit in *Measurement* is preceded by an assessment for that unit. There is also an overall assessment that covers all of the measurement skills in the book. Each of the tests can be used as a pretest to gauge students' areas of strength or weakness. It may also be used as a posttest to demonstrate what students have learned. The overall test can be used as a pretest to give the teacher a clearer picture of the units in which students need the most practice. It can also be used as a posttest to demonstrate improvement or highlight areas that still require attention.

Use

Measurement is designed to complement existing math programs. It is intended for independent use by students who have had instruction in the specific skills covered in the lessons. Copies of the activity sheets can be given to individuals, pairs of students, or groups of students for completion. When students are familiar with the content of the worksheets, they can be assigned as homework.

Determine the implementation that best fits your students' needs and your classroom structure. The following plan suggests a format for implementation.

1. Administer the Overall Assessment to establish baseline information on each student. You may choose to concentrate on certain units after reviewing the test results. Administer the Unit Assessment before beginning a unit. When the unit is finished,

Measurement: Grade 4

Introduction (continued)

you may use the Unit Assessment as a posttest. The Overall Assessment may also be administered after a student, group of students, or the entire class has completed the book. Explain the purpose of the assessments to the class.

2. Explain the purpose of the worksheets to the class.

3. Review the mechanics of how you would like students to work with the activities. Will they work in pairs? Are the activities for homework?

4. Introduce the students to the process and purpose of the activities. Work with students when they have difficulty. Assign only a few pages at a time to avoid pressure.

Additional Notes

Parent Communication—Send the Letter to Parents home with students.

Student Communication—Read the Letter to Students to the class. Answer any questions that arise. Encourage students to share the letter with their parents.

Bulletin Board—Display completed worksheets or projects to show student progress.

Student Progress Chart—Duplicate the grid sheets found on pages 6–7. Record student names in the left column. Note date of completion of each lesson for each student. If students are working independently according to individual areas of weakness, you may wish to highlight the units in which students need practice for convenient reference.

Curriculum Correlation—This chart helps you with cross-curriculum lesson planning.

Have Fun!—Working with these activities should be fun as well as meaningful for you and your students.

Dear Parent,

During this school year, our class will be working with measurement skills. We will be completing activity sheets that will strengthen skills in measurement. We will estimate and measure length, capacity, temperature, and mass. We will study time and money and do computations in measurement.

From time to time, I may send home activity sheets. To best help your child, please consider the following suggestions:

• Provide a quiet place to work.
• Go over the directions on the worksheet together. See that your child understands what is being asked.
• Encourage your child to do his or her best.
• Check the lesson when it is complete.
• Go over your child's work, and note improvements as well as problems.

Help your child maintain a positive attitude about mathematics. Let your child know that each lesson provides an opportunity to have fun and to learn. If your child expresses anxiety about the work, talk to your child about ways to eliminate these feelings. Your relaxed attitude and support will help to reduce your child's anxiety.

Enjoy this time that you spend with your child. With your help, his or her skills will improve with each activity completed.

Thank you for your support!

Cordially,

Dear Student,

An important part of what we do this year in math will be working with measurement. You use measurement many times each day. You may not even think about it. You use measurement when you check the weather, look at the time, or buy your lunch. Measurement is math!

The activities in the measurement book we use will be fun. You will see how learning about measurement can be very useful to you! You may be cooking or guessing the number of jellybeans in a jar. You may be moving the furniture around in your room. All of these things use your skills in measurement.

When you complete a worksheet, remember to:

• Read the directions carefully. What are you being asked to do?
• Read each question carefully. All the questions on a page may not be the same.
• Check your answers when you are finished.

Have fun as you measure your way through math!

Sincerely,

Measurement: Grade 4

Student Progress Chart

STUDENT NAME	UNIT 1 ESTIMATION								UNIT 2 LENGTH											UNIT 3 CAPACITY								UNIT 4 TEMPERATURE							
	13	15	16	17	18	19	20	21	23	24	25	26	27	28	29	30	31	32	33	35	36	37	38	39	40	41	42	43	45	46	47	48	49	50

Measurement: Grade 4

Student Progress Chart

STUDENT NAME	UNIT 5 MASS												UNIT 6 TIME											UNIT 7 MONEY											UNIT 8 COMPUTATION											
	51	53	54	55	56	57	58	59	60	61	62	63	65	66	67	68	69	70	71	72	73	75	76	77	78	79	80	81	82	83	85	86	87	88	89	90	91	92	93	94

www.svschoolsupply.com

© Steck-Vaughn Company

Measurement 4, SV 2068-0

Measurement: Grade 4

Curriculum Correlation

	Social Studies	Physical Education	Science	Art	Language Arts
Unit 1: Estimation					20
Unit 2: Length	32				23, 24, 25, 26, 27, 28, 29, 30, 31,
Unit 3: Capacity			39, 41		35, 36, 37, 38, 39, 40, 41, 42
Unit 4: Temperature	48, 49		45, 46, 47, 48, 49, 50		50
Unit 5: Mass					53, 54, 55, 56, 57, 58, 59, 60, 61
Unit 6: Time		72			65, 66, 67, 68, 69, 70, 71
Unit 7: Money		82			77, 78, 79, 80, 81, 82
Unit 8: Computation				94	86, 89, 91, 93, 94

Name _____ Date _____

Overall Assessment
Measurement, Grade 4

DIRECTIONS

Read each question. Darken the circle for the correct answer.

Unit 1: Estimation

1. What would be the best unit to use to measure the length of a driveway?
- Ⓐ inches
- Ⓑ feet
- Ⓒ miles

2. What would be the best unit to use to measure the amount of juice in a pitcher?
- Ⓐ milliliters
- Ⓑ kiloliters
- Ⓒ liters

3. There are 11 classes at Peterman Elementary School. Each class has 50 minutes of library time each week. About how many hours does the librarian spend with all of the classes each week?
- Ⓐ 13
- Ⓑ 11
- Ⓒ 9

4. Bart bought two baseballs for $3 each, a glove for $21, and a bat for $19. About how much did Bart spend in all?
- Ⓐ $30
- Ⓑ $50
- Ⓒ $40

Unit 2: Length

5. Which of these has a length that is best measured in feet?
- Ⓐ a nail
- Ⓑ a bicycle
- Ⓒ a hamster

6. Mt. Fuji is 3,776 meters high, Mt. Etna is 3,390 meters high, and Mt. Cook is 3,764 meters high. Which mountain peak is the shortest?
- Ⓐ Mt. Fuji
- Ⓑ Mt. Etna
- Ⓒ Mt. Cook

7. Chelsea needs 24 feet of lace for a costume. The lace is sold by the yard. How many yards of lace will Chelsea need to buy?
- Ⓐ 9 yards
- Ⓑ 6 yards
- Ⓒ 8 yards

8. James' stilts are 6 feet tall. Daniel's stilts are 2 yards tall. Whose stilts are taller?
- Ⓐ James' stilts
- Ⓑ Daniel's stilts
- Ⓒ They are the same height.

Go on to the next page.

DIRECTIONS

Read each question. Darken the circle for the correct answer.

Unit 3: Capacity

9. Which would be the best unit to measure the amount of water in a bathtub?
- Ⓐ cups
- Ⓑ gallons
- Ⓒ quarts

10. Connor picked 16 quarts of berries. How many pints of berries did he pick?

- Ⓐ 4
- Ⓑ 32
- Ⓒ 8

11. Gillian has 800 mL of soda in a cup. How much more does she need to fill a 1-L bottle?
- Ⓐ 400 mL
- Ⓑ 20 mL
- Ⓒ 200 mL

12. Harry needs 2 cups of sugar to make brownies. He has 6 cups of sugar. How much extra sugar does Harry have?
- Ⓐ 4 tablespoons
- Ⓑ 4 cups
- Ⓒ 4 teaspoons

Unit 4: Temperature

13. Which is the best estimate of the temperature on a good day to go to the neighborhood pool?
- Ⓐ 45° F
- Ⓑ 62° F
- Ⓒ 88° F

14. When Tia woke up, her thermometer read 12° C. By the afternoon, it had risen to 23° C. How many degrees warmer was it in the afternoon?
- Ⓐ 11° C
- Ⓑ 10° C
- Ⓒ 13° C

15. The water in the town pond is frozen solid and is now safe for skating. What is the best estimate of the temperature outside?
- Ⓐ 43° F
- Ⓑ 59° F
- Ⓒ 28° F

16. A pot of water has just begun to boil. What is the best estimate of the temperature of the water?
- Ⓐ 185° F
- Ⓑ 360° F
- Ⓒ 212° F

Go on to the next page.

Name _____   Date _____

Overall Assessment
Measurement, Grade 4, p. 3

DIRECTIONS

Read each question. Darken the circle for the correct answer.

Unit 5: Mass

17. Mr. Reyna filled 9 seed bags equally with 81 pounds of thistle seeds. How many pounds of thistle seeds fit into each bag?

Ⓐ 9
Ⓑ 18
Ⓒ 72

18. Don's truck can carry 2,000 pounds. He has items that weigh 400 pounds, 350 pounds, and 175 pounds. How much more weight can he carry?

Ⓐ 925 pounds
Ⓑ 1,075 pounds
Ⓒ 75 pounds

19. Which unit of measure would be best to use to find the weight of a tractor?

Ⓐ grams
Ⓑ milligrams
Ⓒ kilograms

20. What is the best estimate of the distance between two cities?

Ⓐ 20 cm
Ⓑ 20 km
Ⓒ 20 m

Unit 6: Time

21. Lupe walked her neighbor's dog 20 minutes a day for 9 weeks. How many hours did Lupe walk the dog?

Ⓐ 21 hours
Ⓑ 8 hours
Ⓒ 180 hours

22. Tim arrives home from school at 3:10 P.M. He goes to bed at 9:00 P.M. How much time does Tim have between arriving home and going to bed?

Ⓐ 5 hours and 10 minutes
Ⓑ 5 hours and 50 minutes
Ⓒ 6 hours and 50 minutes

23. It takes 4 minutes to walk around a track. How long will it take to walk around the track 7 times?

Ⓐ between 10 and 15 minutes
Ⓑ between 15 and 25 minutes
Ⓒ between 25 and 35 minutes

24. It takes Joan 12 seconds to run to the end of her driveway. How many times can Joan run the length of her driveway in 1 minute?

Ⓐ 3
Ⓑ 4
Ⓒ 5

Go on to the next page.

Name _____ Date _____

DIRECTIONS

Read each question. Darken the circle for the correct answer.

Unit 7: Money

25. Keisha bought a package of baseball cards for $1.50, a pen for $3.99, and nail polish for $1.75. About how much did Keisha spend altogether?

Ⓐ $11

Ⓑ $8

Ⓒ $5

26. Joel bought a pencil for 25¢ and an eraser for 9¢. If he paid with $1.00 and tax is included, how much change should he receive?

Ⓐ 66¢

Ⓑ 34¢

Ⓒ 16¢

27. Jill has 2 quarters, 3 dimes, and 5 pennies in her pocket. How much money does she have altogether?

Ⓐ 75¢

Ⓑ 55¢

Ⓒ 85¢

28. Stan has $6.56 in his wallet. Which combination of coins and bills could he have?

Ⓐ 6 dollars, 3 quarters, and 6 pennies

Ⓑ 6 dollars, 5 dimes, and 1 nickel

Ⓒ 6 dollars, 2 quarters, 1 nickel and 1 penny

Unit 8: Computation

29. What is the perimeter of a square that is 3 cm on each side?

Ⓐ 6 cm

Ⓑ 12 cm

Ⓒ 9 cm

30. What is the area of a rectangle that is 6 feet long and 4 feet tall?

Ⓐ 24 square feet

Ⓑ 10 square feet

Ⓒ 20 square feet

31. A pool is 9 meters deep, 10 meters wide, and 13 meters long. What is the volume of the pool?

Ⓐ 1,170 cubic meters

Ⓑ 560 cubic meters

Ⓒ 2,850 cubic meters

32. Bo's room is 9 ft long by 12 ft wide. How many square feet of carpet does he need to cover the floor?

Ⓐ 108

Ⓑ 42

Ⓒ 99

Name _____ Date _____

Unit 1 Assessment
Estimation

DIRECTIONS

Read each problem and solve. Darken the circle for the correct answer.

1. Which unit of measure would be best to determine the length of a soccer field?
   Ⓐ meters
   Ⓑ centimeters
   Ⓒ kilometers

2. Which unit of measure is best to use to describe the weight of an egg?
   Ⓐ tons
   Ⓑ pounds
   Ⓒ ounces

3. Which of these has a weight that is best measured in grams?
   Ⓐ a cookie
   Ⓑ a refrigerator
   Ⓒ a boy

4. Andre went to bed at 9:10 P.M. He woke up at 7:45 A.M. About how many hours did Andre sleep?
   Ⓐ about 10 hours
   Ⓑ about 12 hours
   Ⓒ about 11 hours

5. The temperature outside was too cold for having a picnic, so the students ate their lunch indoors. The temperature was most likely ____ .
   Ⓐ 67° F
   Ⓑ 30° F
   Ⓒ 81° F

6. Mark uses $\frac{1}{2}$ cup of sauce for each pizza he makes. On Friday, he had orders to make 60 pizzas. About how many gallons of sauce did Mark need?
   Ⓐ about 3 gallons
   Ⓑ about 2 gallons
   Ⓒ about 1 gallon

Go on to the next page.

Unit 1 Assessment
Estimation, p. 2

DIRECTIONS

Read each problem and solve. Darken the circle for the correct answer.

7. Sandy has $10.00. She wants to buy 2 tapes at the music store. The tapes cost $5.53 each. About how much more money does she need to buy both tapes?
- Ⓐ about $1.00
- Ⓑ about $5.00
- Ⓒ about $2.00

8. Faoud went shopping for his mother. He bought butter for $1.95, oranges for $2.17, and crackers for $1.89. He gave the cashier $10.00. About how much money should he get back?
- Ⓐ about $6.00
- Ⓑ about $4.00
- Ⓒ about $3.00

9. Julius and his mother bought hot dogs for a picnic. About how many pounds did they probably buy?
- Ⓐ 80 lb
- Ⓑ 800 lb
- Ⓒ 8 lb

10. Which unit of measure would you use to describe the weight of a watermelon?
- Ⓐ kilogram
- Ⓑ centimeter
- Ⓒ liter

11. A rectangle is $4\frac{1}{2}$ inches on one side and 9 inches on the other side. Estimate the perimeter.
- Ⓐ about 30 inches
- Ⓑ about 22 inches
- Ⓒ about 13 inches

12. To set up a science experiment, Kent must first fill 3 test tubes with 3 milliliters of iodine each. About how much iodine does Kent need to fill all 3 tubes?
- Ⓐ about 20 mL
- Ⓑ about 13 mL
- Ⓒ about 10 mL

Name _____ Date _____

What Do You Think?

DIRECTIONS

Circle the more appropriate unit of measure for each example.

1. time needed to buy groceries

minutes or seconds

2. length of a leaf

feet or inches

3. water in a fountain

cups or gallons

4. depth of a well

inches or feet

5. time needed to build a fire

hours or minutes

6. length of a road

yards or miles

7. amount of ice cream in a cone

pints or cups

8. weight of a pack of gum

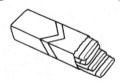

pounds or ounces

9. length of a ball of string

feet or miles

10. weight of an elephant

pounds or tons

11. weight of a pencil

pounds or ounces

12. milk in a carton

teaspoons or pints

Go on to the next page.

What Do You Think?, p. 2

DIRECTIONS

Circle the more appropriate unit of measure for each example.

13. length of a hose

millimeters or meters

14. weight of a ham

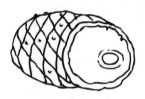

grams or kilograms

15. height of a man

meters or decimeters

16. weight of a sock

grams or milligrams

17. juice of an orange

liters or milliliters

18. length of a banana

centimeters or meters

19. weight of a safe

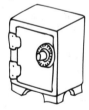

kilograms or grams

20. distance a plane travels

meters or kilometers

21. amount of soup in a pot

liters or kiloliters

22. weight of a paperclip

grams or milligrams

23. height of a tree

meters or kilometers

24. amount of water in a pool

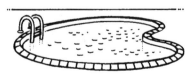

kiloliters or liters

Going to Great Lengths

Choose two more items or areas to measure. Write them in the table. Complete the table with your estimates in customary and metric units. Then measure and prove for both.

Item or Area to Measure	Customary Estimate	Actual Measurement	Metric Estimate	Actual Measurement
pencil				
desk				
chalkboard				
wall of classroom				
length of hallway				

Tools: customary ruler, yardstick, metric ruler, and meter stick

Pouring It On

DIRECTIONS

Describe the item you are filling in the first column of the table. Complete the table with your estimates for customary and metric capacity. Then measure and prove for both.

Item to Fill	Customary Estimate	Actual Capacity	Metric Estimate	Actual Capacity

Tools: measures for milliliters, liters, gallons, quarts, pints, cups, teaspoons, and tablespoons; various unmarked containers such as jars, pails, buckets, test tubes, flasks, pill bottles; water

Name _____ Date _____

Weighing In

Collect six small objects from your classroom, such as a pen, an apple, a bottle of glue, an eraser, and so on. Estimate the weight of each object, and list the objects from what you think is the lightest to what you think is the heaviest on the lines at the bottom of the graph. Then weigh each item. Graph the results. Does your graph line climb steadily? If so, then your estimates were correct!

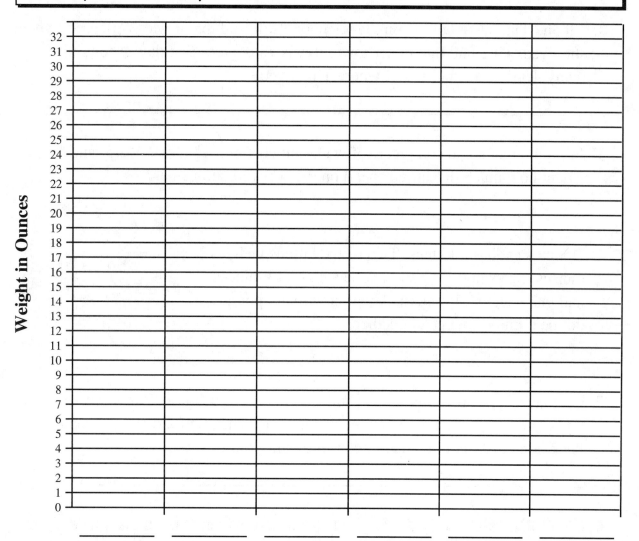

Items Weighed

Tools: ounce scale and variety of small objects as suggested above

Name _____ Date _____

Your Best Guess

DIRECTIONS
Read each problem and solve.

1. Maddy walks a mile in about 17 minutes. If Maddy walks to her grandmother's house 3 miles away, about how long will it take her to get there?

_____

2. Jill and Tina were talking on the telephone. Jill said that it was 37 degrees where she lived. Tina said that in her town, it was 78 degrees that day. About how many degrees warmer was it where Tina lived?

_____

3. Jarred bought some computer software that cost him $24.99, $36.75, and $15.25. About how much did Jarred spend on the software altogether?

_____

4. Donna's cat has 6 kittens. Two of the kittens weigh 12 ounces, two weigh 14 ounces, one weighs 13 ounces, and one weighs 11 ounces. About how many pounds do the 6 kittens weigh altogether?

_____

5. On Saturday, Li rode his bike $1\frac{1}{2}$ miles to his friend's house, 2 more miles to the city park, and $\frac{3}{4}$ of a mile to an ice cream shop. Then he followed the same path back home. About how many miles altogether did Li ride?

_____

6. Tara filled 15 glasses with lemonade for a family picnic. Each glass held 2 cups. About how many quarts of lemonade did Tara need to fill all of the glasses?

_____

Name _____ Date _____

DIRECTIONS

Read each problem and solve. Darken the circle for the correct answer.

1. Julius and his family drove to New Orleans. On the way there, they drove 298 miles. They took a shorter route back and drove 286 miles. How many miles did they drive altogether?
   - Ⓐ 384
   - Ⓑ 484
   - Ⓒ 584

2. Noriko is 53 inches tall, and her younger brother Yuji is 39 inches tall. How much taller is Noriko than Yuji?
   - Ⓐ 14 inches
   - Ⓑ 26 inches
   - Ⓒ 32 inches

3. Joe walks a mile in 15 minutes. If Joe walks for an hour and a half, how many miles can he go?
   - Ⓐ 4 miles
   - Ⓑ 6 miles
   - Ⓒ 8 miles

4. Cathy wants to put fencing around her plants. She needs 11 yards of fencing. The fencing is sold in 15-foot sections. How many sections will Cathy have to buy?
   - Ⓐ 2 sections
   - Ⓑ 3 sections
   - Ⓒ 5 sections

5. Damen's pencil is 5 cm long. How many times would the length of Damen's pencil fit on a meter stick?
   - Ⓐ 20 times
   - Ⓑ 12 times
   - Ⓒ 10 times

6. Perry went on a six-day hiking trip. He hiked the same number of miles each day. By the sixth day, he had gone 42 miles. How many miles did he hike each day?
   - Ⓐ 7 miles
   - Ⓑ 4 miles
   - Ⓒ 8 miles

Go on to the next page.

Tool: pencil

Name _____ Date _____

DIRECTIONS

Read each problem and solve. Darken the circle for the correct answer.

7. How many inches are there between point B and point A?
- Ⓐ 3 in
- Ⓑ $2\frac{1}{2}$ in
- Ⓒ $1\frac{1}{2}$ in

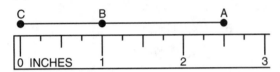

8. How many centimeters are there between point J and point K?
- Ⓐ $1\frac{1}{2}$ cm
- Ⓑ $3\frac{1}{2}$ cm
- Ⓒ 3 cm

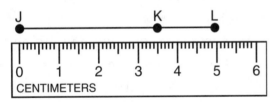

9. Joe's index finger is about 8 cm long. If Joe is 2 meters and 4 cm tall, how many fingers tall would he be?
- Ⓐ $12\frac{1}{2}$ fingers
- Ⓑ $25\frac{1}{2}$ fingers
- Ⓒ $50\frac{1}{2}$ fingers

10. Dharma's favorite race is the 500-yard dash. She holds the record for her school. How many feet does she run?
- Ⓐ 1,500 feet
- Ⓑ 150 feet
- Ⓒ 5,000 feet

11. Tara's hair grows about 1 inch every month. At this rate, how long would it take Tara to grow her hair another foot longer?
- Ⓐ 2 years
- Ⓑ 10 months
- Ⓒ 1 year

12. Ernie is running in a 10-kilometer race. He has already run 7 kilometers. How many more meters will he have to run before he can finish the race?
- Ⓐ 3 meters
- Ⓑ 3,000 meters
- Ⓒ 300 meters

This Tool Rules!

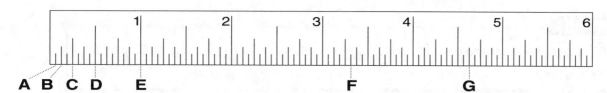

A B C D   E   F   G

This is a section of a customary ruler. It measures length. The markings on the ruler divide it into inches. Each inch is divided into halves, quarters, eighths, and sixteenths.

- The **A** above shows $\frac{1}{16}$ of 1 inch.
- The **B** above shows $\frac{1}{8}$ of 1 inch.
- The **C** above shows $\frac{1}{4}$ of one inch.
- The **D** above shows $\frac{1}{2}$ of one inch.
- The **E** above shows 1 inch exactly.
- What does the **F** show? How many inches does it show? How many parts of an inch? If you say $3\frac{5}{16}$ inches, you are right.
- What does the **G** show? _____

DIRECTIONS

Look at the ruler below. For each letter, write the measurement that is shown.

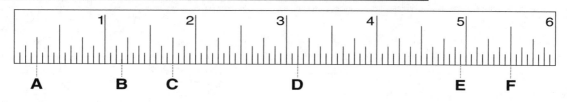

A   B   C   D   E   F

A. _____   B. _____   C. _____   D. _____   E. _____   F. _____

DIRECTIONS

Use a customary ruler to find the length of each item to the nearest $\frac{1}{16}$ of an inch.

1.   2.   3.

_____   _____   _____

Tool: customary ruler

The Long and Short of It

DIRECTIONS

Choose the appropriate unit for each. Write **inches, feet, yards,** or **miles.**

1. The length of an envelope is about

9 ___inches___ .

3. The length of a ramp is about

3 ___yards___ .

2. The height of a tree is about

40 ___feet___ .

4. The height of a mountain is about

9,257 ___feet___ .

DIRECTIONS

Circle the longer unit.

5. 3 ft or (3 yd)   **6.** (16 ft) or 16 in.   **7.** (23 mi) or 23 yd   **8.** 400 in. or (400 yd)

DIRECTIONS

Use the table for Exercises 9-10.

9. Which river is longer than 2,000 miles?

The Mississippi River

10. How long is Snake River?

1,040 miles.

Lengths of U.S. Rivers	
River	**Length in Miles**
Ohio	1,310
Copper	286
Snake	1,040
Mississippi	2,340
Tennessee	886

DIRECTIONS

Solve this problem.

11. Lana lives in Clarkville. She wants to go to Clear Valley by the shortest route. Will she go through Bruster or Capital City? Explain your answer.

Bruster because I estimated the
Sums: Bruster: 280 ; Capital City: 400 miles

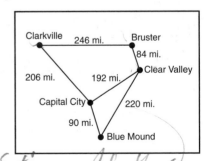

Metric Measures

Circle the more reasonable answer.

1.

   a. 2 cm   **b.** 20 cm

2.

   a. 6 dm   **b.** 6 cm

3.

   a. 1 dm   **b.** 10 dm

Choose the appropriate unit for each. Write **centimeter, decimeter, meter,** or **kilometer.**

4. height of your desk _____

5. height of a flagpole _____

6. length of a road _____

7. length of a calculator _____

Circle the longer unit.

8. 5 cm or 5 dm   **9.** 10 m or 10 dm   **10.** 16 km or 16 dm   **11.** 2 m or 2 cm

Write the number sentence and solve this problem.

12. Enrique swims 7 km a day for 1 week. How many km does he swim in that period of time?

_____

Comparing Measures

DIRECTIONS

Use a ruler. Find the length of each object in centimeters and in inches. Record your measurements.

	Object	Centimeters	Inches
1.	a marker		
2.	a crayon		
3.	a paper clip		
4.	height of your chair		
5.	a folder		
6.	a chalkboard eraser		
7.	a calculator		

8. Use a ruler to draw a rectangle.
The length should be 3 inches.
The width should be 3 centimeters.

DIRECTIONS

Solve these problems.

9. Lee wants to make a picture frame with wood. She needs 96 inches of framing. Lee has two 45-inch strips of wood. Does she have enough wood for the frame? Explain your answer.

_____

_____

10. Would Lee need more or fewer centimeters than inches of wood to frame the same painting?

_____

Tool: customary and metric rulers

Using a Scale

DIRECTIONS

Use the map to estimate the distance to the nearest 500 ft.
Look at the scale for the map. The scale is 500 ft to 1 in.

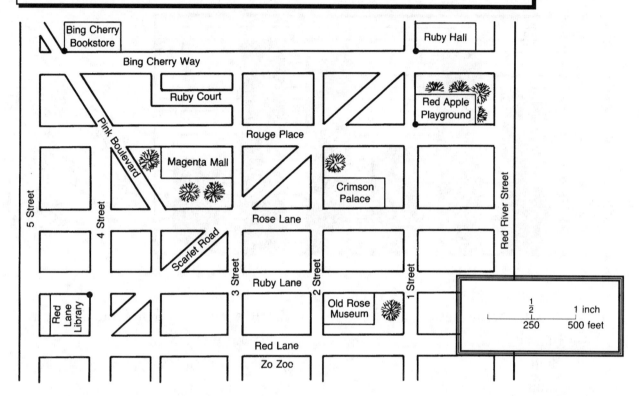

1. What is the distance from Red Lane Library to Ruby Hall if you walk along Scarlet Road?

   _____

2. What is the shortest route from the Red Lane Library at 4th Street and Ruby Lane to the Red Apple Playground at 1st Street and Rouge Place?

   _____

   _____

3. What is the distance from the Old Rose Museum to Magenta Mall if you walk along Ruby Lane and 3rd Street?

   _____

   _____

4. What is the distance from Bing Cherry Bookstore to Zo Zoo if you walk along Bing Cherry Way, 5th Street, and Red Lane?

Tool: customary ruler

Riding for a Cause

DIRECTIONS
Use the graph to answer the following questions.

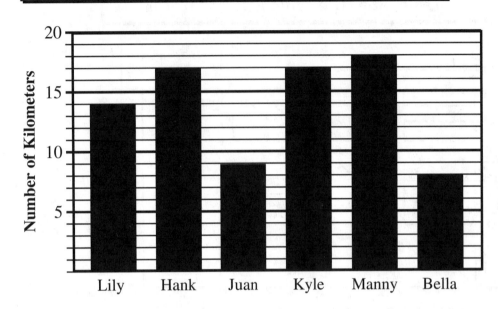

1. Who rode the farthest?
- Ⓐ Bella
- Ⓑ Hank
- Ⓒ Manny

2. How many more kilometers did Kyle ride than Lily?
- Ⓐ 3 kilometers
- Ⓑ 6 kilometers
- Ⓒ 1 kilometer

3. What was the total number of kilometers that the students rode?
- Ⓐ 100 kilometers
- Ⓑ 75 kilometers
- Ⓒ 83 kilometers

4. How many students rode less than 16 kilometers?
- Ⓐ 2 students
- Ⓑ 3 students
- Ⓒ 4 students

5. Hank earned $1.15 for each kilometer he rode. How much money did he earn?
- Ⓐ $25.20
- Ⓑ $15.35
- Ⓒ $19.55

6. At Hank's rate, how much did all of the students earn altogether?
- Ⓐ $95.45
- Ⓑ $74.90
- Ⓒ $83.25

Name _____   Date _____

Miles per Hour

DIRECTIONS

Read the example, then read the questions. Use the map to help you write the answers.

It is easy to measure how fast something travels in 1 hour. Divide the number of miles by the time it takes to travel that distance. Look at the example. You can write miles per hour as *mph*.

$$\frac{90 \text{ miles}}{2 \text{ hours}} = 45 \text{ mph}$$

The Chin family is going on a one-week hiking trip. Look at the map they are using.

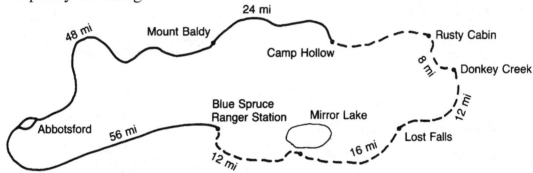

1. The Chin family drove from Mount Baldy to Blue Spruce Ranger Station. They left at 9:00 A.M. and arrived at 11:00 A.M. How many mph did they travel?

_____

2. Arthur hiked from Blue Spruce to Mirror Lake in 3 hours. His parents and his sister Ethel arrived 1 hour later. How many mph did Arthur travel? How many mph did the rest of the Chins travel?

_____

3. On Monday, the Chins hiked from Mirror Lake to Lost Falls in 4 hours. On Tuesday, they hiked from Lost Falls to Rusty Cabin in 4 hours. On which day did they travel faster?

_____

4. On Friday, the Chins were being picked up by a friend at Camp Hollow. They decided they had to travel at 5 mph for 2 hours to meet their friend on time. How many miles did they have to travel?

_____

Name _____ Date _____

A River of Problems

DIRECTIONS

Read each problem and solve.

1. The longest river in China is the Yangtze River. It is three thousand, nine hundred fifteen miles long. Write the number in standard form.

_____

2. Paul has kayaked over 23,572 meters in a weekend race. Write the number of meters in expanded form.

_____

3. The Mississippi River is 2,348 miles long. The Missouri River is 2,315 miles. Write the number sentence using the *greater than* symbol to show which river is longer.

_____

4. Joel's hiking club walked along a river 1,024 meters today. On the day before, they walked 100 meters less than this. Write the number of meters they walked yesterday.

_____

5. The world's longest river is the Nile. It is about 4,160 miles long. Round the length to the nearest hundred miles.

_____

Length's the Word!

1. Lorna has 21 yards of fabric to make a
   bedspread and curtains. If she uses 4 yards to
   make curtains and 13 yards for the bedspread,
   how many yards of fabric will she have left?

   _____

2. Joel needs to repair a second-story window that is 10 meters above the ground.
   His ladder is 2 meters long when folded, but can reach 3 times that distance
   when unfolded. Will his ladder reach the window?

   _____

3. Jamil has an 8-foot board. Can he cut 4 lengths that are each 24 inches long?

   _____

4. A group of mountain climbers climbed a mountain peak that was 897 feet above
   their base camp. Their goal was to reach another peak that was 9,734 feet high.
   How many more feet did they have to climb?

   _____

5. The Cherry Bike Trail is $1\frac{6}{8}$ miles long. The Elm Bike Trail is $\frac{5}{8}$ miles long.
   How much longer is the Cherry Bike Trail than the Elm Bike Trail?

   _____

6. A car dealership has received a shipment of new cars. The cars can travel 36
   miles on each gallon of gas. The gas tanks can hold 18 gallons. Estimate the
   number of miles each car can go on a tank of gas.

   _____

Driving the Distance

DIRECTIONS

The Pecos River is 735 miles long. Starting from your town, use a road atlas to find where you could drive to equal the distance of the Pecos River.

Tool: road atlas

Unit 3 Assessment
Capacity

DIRECTIONS

Read each problem and solve. Darken the circle for the correct answer.

1. What would be the best unit to use to measure the amount of limeade in a pitcher?
   - Ⓐ teaspoon
   - Ⓑ cup
   - Ⓒ quart

2. Which measurement would describe the amount of medicine in a dropper?
   - Ⓐ 6 liters
   - Ⓑ 6 milliliters
   - Ⓒ 6 kiloliters

3. James needs 2 gallons of paint to cover the walls of his room. The color he likes is only available in quart-size cans. How many cans will James need to buy?
   - Ⓐ 4 cans
   - Ⓑ 16 cans
   - Ⓒ 8 cans

4. How many milliliters are there in a 2-liter bottle of soda?
   - Ⓐ 2,000 mL
   - Ⓑ 200 mL
   - Ⓒ 20,000 mL

5. Mrs. Kahn adds 2 cups of water to each container of dry paint for art class. If she has 12 different colors of paint, how many pints of water will she need to get all of the paint ready?
   - Ⓐ 4 pints
   - Ⓑ 8 pints
   - Ⓒ 12 pints

6. The Howe family drinks 2 quarts of milk every three days. How many gallons of milk do the Howes drink in a 30-day month?
   - Ⓐ 4 gallons
   - Ⓑ 5 gallons
   - Ⓒ 10 gallons

Go on to the next page.

Unit 3 Assessment
Capacity, p. 2

DIRECTIONS

Read each problem and solve. Darken the circle for the correct answer.

7. Dianna bought soda for a birthday party. How much soda did she probably buy?
- Ⓐ 8 tablespoons
- Ⓑ 8 quarts
- Ⓒ 8 gallons

8. Kim is making 5 blueberry pies for a bake sale. She needs 4 cups of blueberries for each pie. She has picked 4 quarts of blueberries. How many more quarts does she need to make all 5 pies?
- Ⓐ 1 more quart
- Ⓑ 4 more quarts
- Ⓒ no more quarts

9. Store A is selling orange juice for $3.95 a gallon. Store B is selling orange juice for $1.00 a quart. Which store has the better price on orange juice?
- Ⓐ They are both the same.
- Ⓑ Store A
- Ⓒ Store B

10. Mrs. Garcia told Maria that the baby would drink 3 cups of formula during the time that Maria was baby-sitting. Maria saw that Mrs. Garcia had mixed 1 quart of formula for Maria to put into bottles. Does Maria have enough formula for the baby?
- Ⓐ No, she needs 1 more cup.
- Ⓑ Yes, she has an extra cup.
- Ⓒ Yes, she has the exact amount she needs.

11. Dana drinks 800 mL of water every day. How much water does he drink in 5 days?
- Ⓐ 8 L
- Ⓑ 2 L
- Ⓒ 4 L

12. Jailea uses 2 tablespoons of cocoa powder for each 2-cup mug of hot chocolate she makes. How many tablespoons will she need to make hot chocolate for a group of 12 people?
- Ⓐ 24 tbsp
- Ⓑ 12 tbsp
- Ⓒ 6 tbsp

Pour It On

Directions: Choose the appropriate unit of measure. Write **teaspoon**, **tablespoon**, **cup**, **pint**, **quart**, or **gallon**.

1.

_____

2.

_____

3.

_____

4.

_____

5.

_____

6.

_____

DIRECTIONS
Circle the larger unit.

7. 2 tsp or 2 tbsp

8. 4 pt or 4 c

9. 10 gal or 10 qt

DIRECTIONS
Change each sentence so it makes sense.

10. Ellie uses 4 teaspoons of oatmeal to make cookies.

_____

11. Regan pours a gallon of milk in his glass.

_____

DIRECTIONS
Solve this problem.

12. José pours 1 cup of apple juice and 3 cups of grape juice
into a large bottle. How many pints of juice are in the bottle?

_____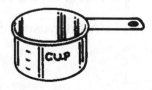

Metric Measures

1.
a large jug of water _____

2.
a bowl of soup _____

3.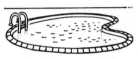
water in a pool _____

4.
a small glass of juice _____

5.
1 mL or 1 L

6.
500 mL or 500 L

7.
120 mL or 120 L

8. A water cooler holds about _____ .
a. 1. 4 mL   **b.** 40 mL   **c.** 4 L

9. A jar of honey holds about _____ .
a. 65 mL   **b.** 650 L   **c.** 65 L

10. A milk carton holds about _____ .
a. 20 mL   **b.** 2 L   **c.** 20 L

11. A tall vase holds about 2 L of water. A wide vase holds about 2,300 mL of water. Which holds more?

_____

Name _____   Date _____

Liquid Measures

DIRECTIONS

With your teacher's help, obtain the following materials:

a set of cup measures $(1, \frac{1}{2}, \frac{1}{3}, \frac{1}{4})$	a 2-quart graduated measure
a set of teaspoon measures $(1, \frac{1}{2}, \frac{1}{4}, \frac{1}{8})$	a gallon jug
	a milliliter measure (graduated cylinder)
a tablespoon	a liter bottle
a 2-cup measure (1 pint)	food coloring

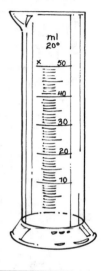

DIRECTIONS

Use colored water to compare the amounts of liquid held by each measure. Then fill in the chart with two possible uses for each type of measure.

Measure	Uses	
cup		
teaspoon		
tablespoon		
pint		
quart		
gallon		
milliliter		
liter		
kiloliter		

Tools: measuring materials as listed, food coloring, water

Liter Log

DIRECTIONS

The fourth-grade students at Connor School are selling liters of soda at ball games to raise money. They make $0.35 on each 1-liter bottle they sell. The graph below shows their sales for the months of September and October. Use the graph to answer the questions.

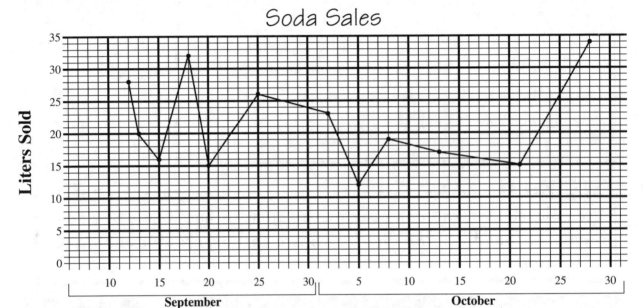

Soda Sales

Liters Sold

September   October

Dates of Sales

1. On what day did the students sell the most soda?

   _____

2. During which month did the students make the most money? _____

3. Between which 2 consecutive games was there the greatest difference in sales?

   _____

4. On which 2 days was the same amount sold?

   _____

5. How much money did the students make for the 2 months together? _____

Keeping It Clean

DIRECTIONS

There are 4 rivers that flow off of Redstone Mountain. Redstone park rangers test the water every day to see if it is polluted. They test the water at several different places along each river. Below is a map of each test spot and how much water is taken out for each test. Use the map to solve the problems below.

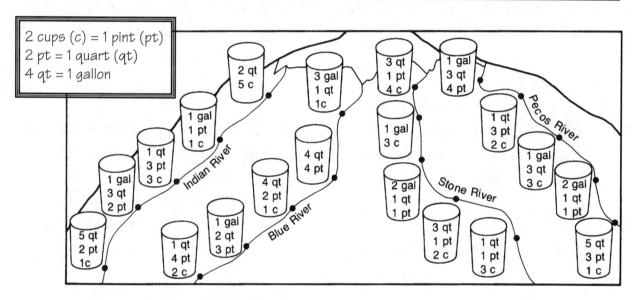

2 cups (c) = 1 pint (pt)
2 pt = 1 quart (qt)
4 qt = 1 gallon

1. How much water is taken out of the Blue River every day?

_____

2. Which river has the least amount of water taken out each day? How much?

_____

3. Which river has the greatest amount of water taken out each day? How much?

_____

4. How much more water is taken out of the Pecos River than the Indian River?

_____

5. Which 2 rivers have about the same amount of water taken out each day?

_____

6. How much water is taken out of all 4 rivers in one day?

_____

A Question of Capacity

DIRECTIONS

Read each problem and solve.

1. Mr. Burns is painting his living room. He mixes 2 pints of red paint, 1 quart of blue paint, and 2 quarts of white paint. How many gallons of paint does Mr. Burns have?

   _____

2. Nina used $\frac{2}{3}$ cup of sugar in her apple muffins. Laurel used $\frac{5}{8}$ cup of sugar in her apple muffins. How much more sugar did Nina use?

   _____

3. John saw that the water was low in his 10-gallon aquarium. He had to add 3 quarts of water to fill it again. How much water was in John's aquarium when he saw that it was low?

   _____

4. Tina used a gallon jug to water the plants in her house. She emptied the jug once, filled it again, and had 3 cups of water left over. How much water did Tina use to water her plants?

   _____

5. At the pet store, each hamster cage has a 225 mL water bottle. There are 8 hamster cages at the store. About how many L of water does it take to fill all of the water bottles?

   _____

6. Geoff drinks 8 ounces of orange juice every morning. How many pints of orange juice does Geoff drink in a 28-day period?

   _____

Tempt Your Taste Buds

DIRECTIONS

Look at the 2 drink recipes below. Compare the amounts of the ingredients used in each. Then answer the questions.

Creamy Punch

$1\frac{1}{2}$-ounce envelope lemon-lime or cherry-
   flavored soft drink mix (unsweetened)

1 c granulated sugar

2 c milk

1 quart sherbet or vanilla ice cream

$3\frac{1}{2}$ c carbonated water

In a 2-quart pitcher, mix dry ingredients. Stir in milk until dissolved. Pour mixture into 6–8 glasses, about $\frac{3}{4}$ full. Add a scoop or two of ice cream to each glass. Add soda water slowly to each glass until the glass is filled. Place a long spoon in each glass, or stir each one just slightly.

Fruity Cooler

$1\frac{1}{2}$-ounce envelope raspberry-flavored
   soft drink mix (unsweetened)

$\frac{3}{4}$ c granulated sugar

4 c cold water

$\frac{1}{2}$ c orange juice

$\frac{1}{4}$ c lemon juice

$1\frac{1}{2}$ c pineapple juice

In a 2-quart pitcher, mix dry ingredients in water until dissolved. Add fruit juices. Place in refrigerator for about 1 hour. Makes 4–6 servings.

---

1. Which recipe uses more dry ingredients?

_____

2. Which recipe uses more liquid ingredients?

_____

3. Choose one recipe and double it. How much of each ingredient would you need?

_____

4. About how many servings would your doubled recipe make?

_____

Cups in a Cooler

DIRECTIONS

You are supposed to take 5 gallons of water to a game. You are not sure how much water your cooler will hold. With an 8-ounce cup, how can you determine the amount of water your cooler will hold?

Name _____ Date _____

Unit 4 Assessment
Temperature

DIRECTIONS

Read each problem and solve. Darken the circle for the correct answer.

1. Which temperature does the thermometer show?

Ⓐ 45° F
Ⓑ 50° F
Ⓒ 47° F

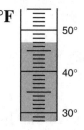

2. Which temperature does the thermometer show?

Ⓐ 12° F
Ⓑ 10° F
Ⓒ 15° F

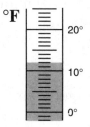

3. Which temperature does the thermometer show?

Ⓐ 90° F
Ⓑ 93° F
Ⓒ 95° F

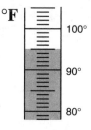

4. Which temperature does the thermometer show?

Ⓐ 30° C
Ⓑ 3° C
Ⓒ 5° C

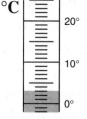

5. Which temperature does the thermometer show?

Ⓐ 15° C
Ⓑ 20° C
Ⓒ 5° C

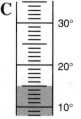

6. Which temperature does the thermometer show?

Ⓐ 30° C
Ⓑ 45° C
Ⓒ 35° C

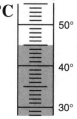

Go on to the next page.

Unit 4 Assessment
Temperature, p. 2

DIRECTIONS

Read each problem and solve. Darken the circle for the correct answer.

7. The students at Clancy Elementary School will not go outside for recess if the temperature drops below 25° F today. At 8:00 A.M., it was 32° F. The temperature has been dropping 2 degrees every hour. If it continues to drop at this rate, what will the temperature be at 1:00 P.M. when it is time for recess?

Ⓐ 42° F

Ⓑ 22° F

Ⓒ 24° F

8. Brent is making cookies that should bake at 375° F. His oven has heated to 220° F. How many more degrees does it need to heat before Brent can put in a tray of cookies?

Ⓐ 145° F

Ⓑ 255° F

Ⓒ 155° F

9. Tony can only paint outside if it is above freezing. On Monday, the temperature was -5° C, on Tuesday, it was 0° C, on Wednesday it was 5° C, on Thursday it was 3° C, and on Friday it was -2° C. How many days could Tony paint outside this week?

Ⓐ 1 day

Ⓑ 2 days

Ⓒ 3 days

10. What would be the best estimate of the temperature of a cup of hot chocolate?

Ⓐ 110° F

Ⓑ 212° F

Ⓒ 68° F

11. Brian says that his thermometer reaches the boiling point at 212° F. Rick says that his thermometer reaches the boiling point at 100° C. Which boy is correct?

Ⓐ Brian

Ⓑ Rick

Ⓒ Both of them

12. The temperature outside is 58° F. What type of activity should Susan plan with her friends?

Ⓐ swimming in the lake

Ⓑ taking a hike

Ⓒ ice-skating on the town pond

Think Thermometers

DIRECTIONS

Write the temperature that is shown on each thermometer.

1. 60°
50°

2. 95°
90°
85°

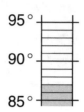

3. 45°
35°

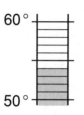 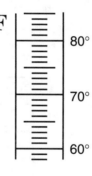 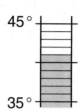

_____   _____   _____

DIRECTIONS

Fill in the thermometer to show the temperature for each example.

4. °F
50°
40°
30°

46° F

5. °F
80°
70°
60°

68° F

6. °F
40°
30°
20°

34° F

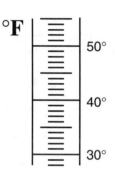 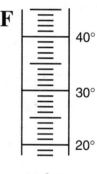

7. °F
40°
30°
20°

28° F

8. °F
60°
50°
40°

56° F

9. °F
100°
90°
80°

88° F

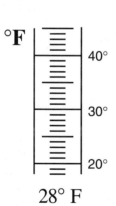 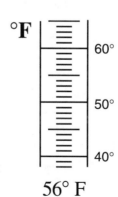 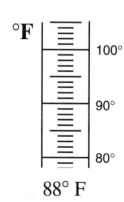

Go on to the next page.

Measurement 4, SV 2068-0

Name _____ Date _____

Think Thermometers, p. 2

DIRECTIONS
Write the temperature that is shown on each thermometer.

10.
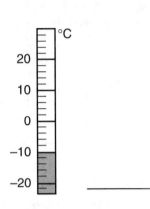

11.
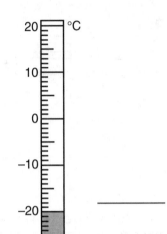

12.
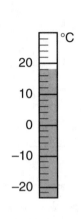

DIRECTIONS
Fill in the thermometer to show the temperature for each example.

13.
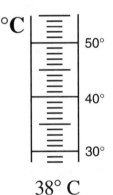
38° C

14.
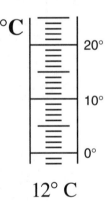
12° C

15.
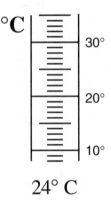
24° C

16.
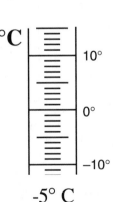
-5° C

17.
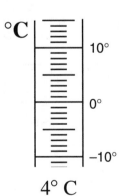
4° C

18.
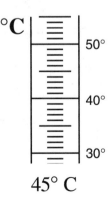
45° C

River Town Temps

DIRECTIONS
Use the graph to answer questions 1-6.

River Town's Average Temperature

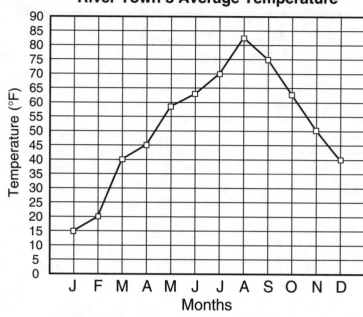

1. What was the average temperature in December? _____

2. Which 2 months had the same average temperature? _____

3. In which month was the average temperature 70° F? _____

4. Between which 2 months was the greatest increase in temperature? _____

5. What was the temperature in the first month, and to what temperature
   did it increase? _____

6. What was the highest recorded temperature? _____
   The lowest? _____

Name _____   Date _____

March in Miami

DIRECTIONS

The table shows the average temperatures for October through March in Miami, Florida. Complete the line graph to show how the temperature changed. Then use the graph to answer the questions.

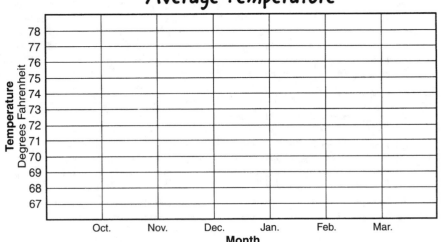

Month	Average Temperature
October	78° F
November	72° F
December	68° F
January	67° F
February	68° F
March	71° F

1. Between which 2 months did the average temperature change the most?

_____

2. By how many degrees did it differ? _____

3. Was the change an increase or a decrease in temperature? _____

4. During which 2 months was the temperature the same?

_____

5. What was the highest recorded average temperature? _____

6. During which month was the highest temperature recorded? _____

Name _____ Date _____

Keeping Track of Temperature

DIRECTIONS

A group of students kept track of the high temperature in Celsius degrees in their town for one month. They wrote their results on a calendar. Use the calendar to answer questions 1-4.

High Temperatures for May (° C)

Mon	Tue	Wed	Thu	Fri	Sat	Sun
	1 5°	2 7°	3 10°	4 8°	5 6°	6 11°
7 10°	8 8°	9 13°	10 15°	11 20°	12 23°	13 27°
14 30°	15 31°	16 33°	17 25°	18 27°	19 23°	20 25°
21 26°	22 26°	23 28°	24 30°	25 35°	26 34°	27 35°
28 33°	29 34°	30 30°	31 31°			

1. On which day was the lowest temperature? _____

2. Which 2 days had the highest temperature? _____

3. Which days would be the best for swimming? _____

4. Would you be more likely to wear a coat on the 24th or on the 5th? _____

5. Keep track of the temperature outside your school or home for 2 weeks. Put your results on a graph. You may use a Celsius or a Fahrenheit thermometer. Compare your results with your classmates' results.

Tools: Celsius or Fahrenheit thermometer, graph paper

Name _____ Date _____

Keep Your Cool

DIRECTIONS
Read each problem and solve.

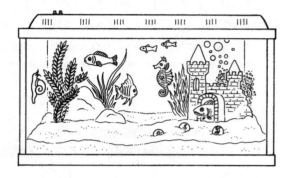

1. When Jenny woke up, it was 58° F. By 1:00, the temperature had risen 14° F. What was the temperature at 1:00?

   _____

2. Gerard had planned a trip to the beach for Thursday. On Wednesday evening, the weather report said that the high for Thursday would be 13° C. Should Gerard have stayed with his beach plans or made plans for another type of activity? Why?

   _____

   _____

   _____

3. Suzanne has 2 pots of water on the stove. One is heated to 98° C. The other is heated to 190° F. In which pot is the water closer to boiling?

   _____

4. The water in Kendra's fish tank should stay between 72° F and 78° F at all times. Kendra has just cleaned the tank and is adding hot water to the cool water in the tank, which is at 56° F. Each time she adds a quart of hot water, the temperature rises 4° F. If she adds 5 quarts of hot water, will the temperature in her tank be safe for her fish? What will it be?

   _____

   _____

5. Raoul is testing the temperature of 2 trays of water from his freezer. One tray measures 5° C. The other measures 33° F. In which tray is the water closer to freezing?

   _____

Name _____ Date _____

Unit 5 Assessment
Mass

DIRECTIONS
Read each problem and solve. Darken the circle for the correct answer.

1. What would be the best unit to use to measure the weight of a person?
   Ⓐ ounces
   Ⓑ pounds
   Ⓒ tons

2. What would be the best unit to use to measure the weight of a peach?
   Ⓐ grams
   Ⓑ kilograms
   Ⓒ milligrams

3. Which would be the best estimate of the weight of a car?
   Ⓐ 1,750 ounces
   Ⓑ 1,750 tons
   Ⓒ 1,750 pounds

4. Which would be the best estimate of the weight of a can of soup?
   Ⓐ 350 milligrams
   Ⓑ 350 grams
   Ⓒ 350 kilograms

5. Kyra's dog weighs 38 pounds. Her brother's dog weighs 23 pounds. How much heavier is Kyra's dog than her brother's dog?
   Ⓐ 15 pounds
   Ⓑ 17 pounds
   Ⓒ 24 pounds

6. The school lunchroom uses 33 pounds of fruit each day. About how many ounces does the school use each day?
   Ⓐ about 500
   Ⓑ about 700
   Ⓒ about 300

Go on to the next page.

Unit 5 Assessment
Mass, p. 2

DIRECTIONS

Read each problem and solve. Darken the circle for the correct answer.

7. Beth buys equal parts of 4 kinds of nails. The total weight of the nails is 2 pounds. How many ounces of each kind of nail does Beth buy?

Ⓐ 4 ounces

Ⓑ 16 ounces

Ⓒ 8 ounces

8. Karen needs 1 kilogram of flour. She has 275 grams. How much more flour does Karen need?

Ⓐ 825 grams

Ⓑ 725 grams

Ⓒ 650 grams

9. Bananas are 56 cents a pound. If Kerri buys 80 ounces of bananas, how much will she pay for them in all?

Ⓐ $2.80

Ⓑ $3.00

Ⓒ $44.80

10. Each shelf in Alan's bookcase can hold 63 pounds of books. Alan has 175 pounds of books to put on the three shelves. Can the bookcase hold all of Alan's books?

Ⓐ Yes, the bookcase can hold over 200 pounds of books.

Ⓑ Yes, the bookcase can hold 189 pounds of books.

Ⓒ No, the bookcase can only hold 126 pounds of books.

11. Jane weighs 67 pounds and 4 ounces with her boots on. She weighs 65 pounds and 2 ounces without her boots on. How much do Jane's boots weigh?

Ⓐ 2 pounds and 1 ounce

Ⓑ 2 pounds and 4 ounces

Ⓒ 2 pounds and 2 ounces

12. Tran's dog weighs 10 kilograms. Three months ago, he weighed only $3\frac{1}{2}$ kilograms. How much weight has Tran's dog gained?

Ⓐ $7\frac{1}{2}$ kilograms

Ⓑ 6 kilograms

Ⓒ $6\frac{1}{2}$ kilograms

Name _____ Date _____

Weighing In

DIRECTIONS
Choose the appropriate unit to measure. Write **ounce**, **pound**, or **ton**.

1.

2.

3.

_____   _____   _____

4.

5.

6.

_____   _____   _____

DIRECTIONS
Circle the more reasonable measurement.

7.

8.

9.

1 oz or 1 lb   7 lb or 70 lb   5 oz or 25 oz

DIRECTIONS
Complete. You may use a calculator.

10. 5 lb = _____ oz   **11.** 13 T = _____ lb   **12.** 64 oz = _____ lb

DIRECTIONS
Solve this problem.

13. Rose's family recipe for muffins calls for 12 ounces of chopped apples to serve 4 people. How many pounds of chopped apples should Rose add to the batter to serve 16 people?

_____

| **Tool: calculator** |

Heavyweights or Lightweights?

DIRECTIONS

Choose the appropriate unit to weigh each item.
Write **grams** or **kilograms**.

1.
_____

2.
_____

3.
_____

4.
_____

5.
_____

6.
_____

DIRECTIONS

Circle the more reasonable measurement.

7.

a feather

1 g or 100 g

8.

a truck

175 kg or 1,750 kg

9.

a pair of gloves

20 g or 200 g

10.

a piano

40 kg or 450 kg

DIRECTIONS

Write the number sentence and solve this problem.

11. Karen needs 1 kilogram of flour. She has 275 grams.
How much more flour does Karen need?

_____

FLOUR

Way to Weigh

DIRECTIONS

Rename the weight. Choose from grams (g) to kilograms (kg).

1.

Beaver = 22,000 g

8 Beavers = _____ kg

2.

Fox = 10,000 g

10 Foxes = _____ kg

3.

Rabbit = 4,000 g

13 Rabbits = _____ kg

4.

Woodchuck = 9,000 g

7 Woodchucks = _____ kg

5.

Skunk = 7,000 g

11 Skunks = _____ kg

6.

Raccoon = 16,000 g

9 Raccoons = _____ kg

7. List the animals from the heaviest to the lightest.

_____

_____

8. Why is it easier to measure large animals in kilograms than in grams?

_____

_____

How's Your Balance?

DIRECTIONS

Choose 5 items in the classroom. Using only a balance, find which item weighs the most. Which item weighs the least? List the items in order from the heaviest to the lightest. Then explain how you determined the order.

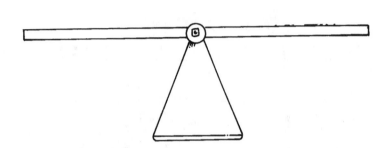

1. _____

2. _____

3. _____

4. _____

5. _____

Explanation

_____

_____

_____

_____

_____

_____

_____

_____

_____

Tools: balance, various items to weigh

Estimate Weight

DIRECTIONS

Use estimation to help you circle the weight
that will balance each scale.

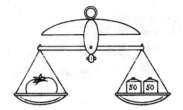

1. 733 g | 596 g (?) | 37 g | 137 g | 497 g

2. 4,592 g | 3,022 g (?) | 1,570 g | 570 g | 4,647 g

3. 13 kg (?) | 38 kg | 49 kg | 25 kg | 16 kg

4. 47 kg (?) | 92 kg | 22 kg | 60 kg | 45 kg

5. 1,321 mg (?) | 3,783 mg | 2,462 mg | 3,400 mg | 2,595 mg

6. 52 mg | 22 mg (?) | 41 mg | 38 mg | 30 mg

7. 12 kg | 1,000 g (?) | 11,000 g | 10,000 g | 13,000 g

8. 40 kg (?) | 80,000 g | 80 kg | 20 kg | 40 kg

Measurement 4, SV 2068-0

Name _____   Date _____

Winning Weights

DIRECTIONS

Read the story, then look at the list of prizes for the Corny Corn Flake Company. Each letter equals a weight on the postage scale. Use the postage scale to complete the table.

The cost of mailing a package depends on how much it weighs. Mail in the United States is weighed in pounds and ounces.

The Corny Corn Flake Company had a contest. The company is using the Stamp-and-Go Mail Service to send prizes to winners. Look at the mailing rate. The example shows how much it would cost the Corny Corn Flake Company to send a 3-ounce package to a winner.

First ounce = 9 cents	1 oz at 9 cents	= 9 cents
Each additional ounce = 7 cents	2 oz at 7 cents each	= 14 cents
	Total mailing cost	= 23 cents

Prize	Weight
Corny Corn Flakes T-shirt	a
Corny Corn Flakes mug	b
CD of Corny Songs	c
Corny Corn Game	d

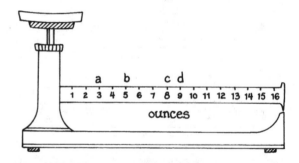

Winner	Prizes	Total oz	Cost of first oz	Cost of additional ounces	Total mailing cost
Jane	CD and T-shirt		9¢		
Ralph	Game		9¢		
Maria	Mug		9¢		
Lin	T-shirt and mug		9¢		
Claus	CD and mug		9¢		

Name _____   Date _____

It's a Boy!

DIRECTIONS

Use the graph to answer the questions. Darken the circle for the correct answer.

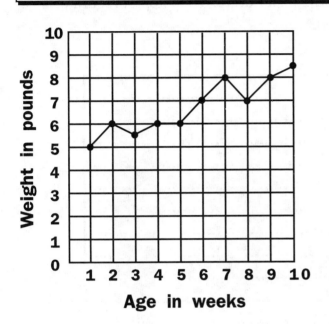

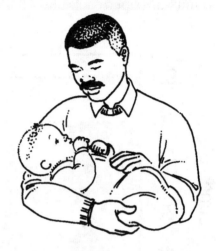

3. How much did the baby gain between 4 weeks and 6 weeks?
Ⓐ 2 pounds
Ⓑ 1 pound
Ⓒ 0 pounds

1. The graph shows the growth of Mr. and Mrs. Tosca's baby. How old was the baby when he weighed $5\frac{1}{2}$ pounds?
Ⓐ 3 weeks
Ⓑ 1 week
Ⓒ 5 weeks

4. During which week did the baby lose $\frac{1}{2}$ pound?
Ⓐ week 3
Ⓑ week 2
Ⓒ week 4

2. How old was the baby when he weighed 8 pounds?
Ⓐ 10 weeks
Ⓑ 6 weeks
Ⓒ 7 weeks

5. During which 2-week period did the baby gain the most weight?
Ⓐ weeks 2–4
Ⓑ weeks 5–7
Ⓒ weeks 3–5

Pounds of Paper

Use the graph to answer the questions.

The students at Edgemont School held a paper drive. They kept a record of how many pounds of paper each class collected.

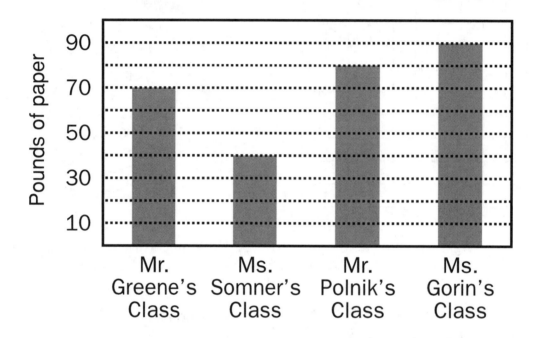

1. How many pounds of paper did Ms. Somner's class collect?

_____

2. How many pounds of paper were collected by all four classes?

_____

3. How many more pounds of paper did Ms. Gorin's class collect than Mr. Greene's class?

_____

4. Which class collected the least amount of paper?

_____

5. How many more pounds of paper did Mr. Polnik's class collect than Ms. Somner's class?

_____

6. How many pounds of paper did Ms. Gorin's class collect?

_____

Name _____ Date _____

Weigh to Go!

DIRECTIONS
Read each problem and solve.

1. Mr. Reyna filled 9 seed bags equally with 81 pounds of sunflower seeds. How many pounds of sunflower seeds fit into each bag?

   _____

2. Clark and Sara are members of a 4-H Club. They raise cattle. Clark's calf weighs 87 pounds. Sara's calf weighs 72 pounds. How much heavier is Clark's calf than Sara's calf?

   _____

3. Diego's German shepherd puppy weighs 17.39 kilograms. What is the puppy's weight rounded to the nearest kilogram?

   _____

4. Eight members of a club are going backpacking. They plan to take 96 pounds of gear with them. They each want to carry an equal amount. How much will each person carry?

   _____

5. Richard needs 1 kilogram of bird seed. He has 400 grams. How much more bird seed does Richard need?

   _____

6. When Gordon was born, he weighed 10 pounds. Now he weighs 72 pounds. How much weight has Gordon gained since he was born?

   _____

Postage Problem

Rita wants to mail 3 presents to her grandchildren in another state. One present weighs 4 pounds, one weighs 7 pounds, and the third weighs 28 pounds. Using the chart, what is the least expensive way for Rita to mail the gifts? How much will she pay?

WINDOW NO. 3

STAMPS

PACKAGE RATES	
POUNDS	COST
0 – 5	$2
5 – 10	$3
10 – 15	$4
15 – 20	$5
20 – 30	$7
30 – 40	$9

ZIP CODE YOUR MAIL

NEW STAMP RATES

Name _____   Date _____

Unit 6 Assessment
Time

DIRECTIONS

Read each problem and solve. Darken the circle for the correct answer. Use the graph to answer questions 1-6.

Lena's Baby-sitting Record

3. How many hours did Lena baby-sit on Monday?
Ⓐ 1 hour
Ⓑ 0 hours
Ⓒ 2 hours

4. On which day did Lena baby-sit the most number of hours?
Ⓐ Saturday
Ⓑ Sunday
Ⓒ Friday

1. Lena kept a graph to show how many hours she baby-sat in 1 week. How many hours did Lena baby-sit for the whole week?
Ⓐ 10 hours
Ⓑ 8 hours
Ⓒ 13 hours

5. How many more hours did Lena baby-sit on Friday than she did on Monday?
Ⓐ 2 hours
Ⓑ 3 hours
Ⓒ 1 hour

2. Lena baby-sat for 2 hours on Sunday. On which other day did she baby-sit the same amount of time?
Ⓐ Tuesday
Ⓑ Wednesday
Ⓒ Thursday

6. If Lena makes $3.50 per hour, how much did she make this week altogether?
Ⓐ $45.50
Ⓑ $38.00
Ⓒ $52.50

Go on to the next page.

Unit 6 Assessment
Time, p. 2

DIRECTIONS

Read each problem and solve. Darken the circle for the correct answer.

7. What time is it 3 hours after 11:00 A.M.?
- Ⓐ 2:00 P.M.
- Ⓑ 2:00 A.M.
- Ⓒ 3:00 P.M.

8. The average person breathes once every 4 seconds. About how many breaths does a person take in half a minute?
- Ⓐ about 15
- Ⓑ about 6
- Ⓒ about 8

9. It usually takes 3 minutes for each car to go through the car wash. What is a good estimate of how long it will take 7 cars to go through the car wash?
- Ⓐ between 10 and 15 minutes
- Ⓑ between 15 and 25 minutes
- Ⓒ between 25 and 35 minutes

10. The movie starts at 4:30. The picture shows Jean's watch. How many minutes will it be until the movie begins?
- Ⓐ 20 minutes
- Ⓑ 25 minutes
- Ⓒ 30 minutes

11. What time will it be in 50 minutes?
- Ⓐ 7:00
- Ⓑ 7:10
- Ⓒ 6:50

12. If it is 10:45 A.M. now, and Simon goes swimming in $2\frac{1}{2}$ hours, what time will it be when he goes swimming?
- Ⓐ 1:15 P.M.
- Ⓑ 1:45 P.M.
- Ⓒ 1:30 P.M.

Name _____   Date _____

Judging Time

DIRECTIONS

Choose the most reasonable unit of time for each.
Write **second, minute, hour, day, week, month, or year.**

1.

Summer lasts about 3
_____.

2.

It takes about 10 _____
to take a shower.

3.

To eat your breakfast takes
about 20 _____.

4.

It takes about one _____
to tear paper.

DIRECTIONS

Choose the best estimate for each.

5. The time it takes to set up a tent.
  Ⓐ 15 minutes
  Ⓑ 5 hours
  Ⓒ 5 days

6. The time it takes to get a good
  night's sleep.
  Ⓐ 8 seconds
  Ⓑ 80 minutes
  Ⓒ 8 hours

DIRECTIONS

Solve this problem.

7. Jeff thought his piano lesson would last about one
  hour. His lesson started at 2:55 P.M. About what
  time will his lesson be over?

_____

Name _____ Date _____

Watching the Clock

DIRECTIONS
Write the time in two different ways.

1.

_____

_____

2.

_____

_____

3.

_____

_____

4.

_____

_____

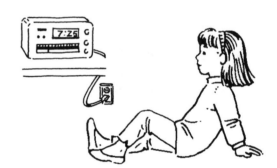

DIRECTIONS
Match the time with the clock.

5. five minutes past three

6. fifteen minutes to five

3:05

4:45

DIRECTIONS
Solve this problem.

7. Jim preheated the oven at 3:00. Jason prepared the bread dough at 2:50. Helen put some rolls in the oven at quarter past three. Which activity took place first?

_____

Keeping Time

DIRECTIONS

Tell how much time has elapsed.

1.

Begin A.M.   End P.M.

_____

2.

Begin A.M.   End P.M.

_____

DIRECTIONS

Use the clocks to help you answer Exercises 3-5.

3.

How many minutes pass from
1:20 P.M. to 1:55 P.M.?

_____

4.

How many hours pass from
9:00 A.M. to 2:00 P.M.?

_____

5.

What is the time when it is
30 minutes before 8:15 A.M.?

_____

DIRECTIONS

Solve this problem.

6. Luis went outside to ride his bike at 3:35 P.M. His
mother told him to be home by 4:10 P.M. How long did
Luis have to ride his bike?

_____

Name _____ Date _____

Adver-timing

DIRECTIONS

WWIN-TV's five programs on Saturday morning are Howdy Boys, Young Scientists, Hound Dog Jones, Jumping Jacks, and Around the Corner. The television station made a table to show which commercials appear during each show. Use the table to solve Exercises 1–4.

	60 s = 1 min
	30 s x 2 = 1 min
	15 s x 4 = 1 min

	Howdy Boys 8:00—8:30	Young Scientists 8:30—9:30	Hound Dog Jones 9:30—10:00	Jumping Jacks 10:00—11:00	Around the Corner 11:00—12:00
Real Fruit Juice = 1 min					
Hungry Muffins = 30 s					
Gain Toothbrush = 30 s					
Super Boots = 15 s					

1. Gain Toothbrush wants the same amount of commercial time as Hungry Muffins. How many more commercials do they need?

_____

2. If you watched WWIN-TV from 8:00 A.M. until 12:00 noon, how many minutes of commercials would you see?

_____

3. How many minutes of commercials for Real Fruit Juice are shown?

_____

4. Which half-hour show has the least number of commercials? How many minutes?

_____

Name _____ Date _____

Fun Fair

DIRECTIONS

Study the schedule. Then answer the questions.

County Fair — Children's Events				
	11:00–12:00	1:00	2:00	3:00
FRI	Judging of 4-H craft projects	Footraces - - - - - - - →		
		Toddlers	4–5 year-olds	6–8 year-olds
SAT	Pet Parade	Footraces - - - - - - - →		
	Judging of 4-H farming projects	9–10 year-olds	11–12 year-olds	13–14 year-olds
				Teddy bear picnic
SUN	Baby contest	Crowning of	Marching band	
	Judging of 4-H	4-H king	contest	
	livestock projects	and queen		

1. For how many days will there be children's events?

_____

2. What time will the marching band contest start?

_____

3. Which group will be in the footraces on Friday at 3:00?

_____

4. When will the 4-H king and queen be crowned?

_____

5. How long do the footraces last?

_____

6. What begins on Sunday, 3 hours before the marching band contest?

_____

Name _____   Date _____

Chores Galore

List 5 chores you must do at home or school. Estimate the amount of time it takes to complete each chore. Then time yourself the next time you do the chores. Did it take more or less time than you estimated? Is there a way you could do the chores more quickly?

	Chore	Time Estimate	Actual Time
1.			
2.			
3.			
4.			
5.			

Tool: clock

Show Time!

DIRECTIONS

Look in the newspaper for a movie you would like to see. Choose a time to go see this movie. Then plan a schedule for how long it would take to get ready for the movie, pick up 2 other friends, and arrive in time to buy tickets and snacks and to find seats before the movie starts. Write your schedule in the space provided.

Tool: newspaper

Are You a Couch Potato?

DIRECTIONS

Keep a record of how many hours of television you watch in 1 week. Think of a good way to organize your information. Based on your findings, how much television do you watch in 1 month? How much do you watch in 1 year? Do your findings surprise you?

Tools: television, clock

Name _____ Date _____

Unit 7 Assessment
Money

DIRECTIONS

Read each problem and solve. Darken the circle for the correct answer.

1. Clark had 3 quarters, 4 dimes, 2 nickels, and 3 pennies in his pocket. He bought a candy bar for 63 cents. How much money does Clark have left in his pocket?

Ⓐ 35 cents

Ⓑ 65 cents

Ⓒ 26 cents

2. Jeannie has 73 cents on her desk. Which of these could NOT be the coins that are on Jeannie's desk?

Ⓐ 3 quarters, 3 pennies

Ⓑ 1 half-dollar, 2 dimes, 3 pennies

Ⓒ 2 quarters, 4 nickels, 3 pennies

3. Jill had $2.85 in her purse. As she walked to the store, she found 2 quarters, a dime, and 6 pennies on the ground. How much money does Jill have now?

Ⓐ $3.01

Ⓑ $3.96

Ⓒ $3.51

4. Fiona wants to buy a stereo that costs $99.95, tax included. She has saved $55.49. How much more money does Fiona need to buy the stereo?

Ⓐ $44.46

Ⓑ $45.59

Ⓒ $54.45

5. Angela bought a set of paints for $7.84 and a new canvas for $5.99, tax included. How much did she spend on her purchases?

Ⓐ $12.73

Ⓑ $13.82

Ⓒ $13.83

6. Jonah bought a roll of film for $5.20, photo album for $7.99, and batteries for $4.15. The tax was $0.86. If Jonah paid with a $20 bill, how much change did he get back?

Ⓐ $2.66

Ⓑ $1.80

Ⓒ $1.95

Go on to the next page.

Name _____ Date _____

DIRECTIONS

Read each problem and solve. Darken the circle for the correct answer.

7. Drew gets $3.00 an hour for baby-sitting 1 child, and $4.00 an hour for baby-sitting 2 children. She baby-sat for 26 hours in the month of July. Half of the time she watched 1 child, and the other half of the time she watched 2 children. How much money did she make?

Ⓐ $182.00

Ⓑ $70.00

Ⓒ $91.00

8. A movie ticket costs $7.25 for adults and $6.50 for children. If the Smith family of 2 adults and 3 children go to a movie, how much will the tickets cost altogether?

Ⓐ $34.00

Ⓑ $27.50

Ⓒ $36.25

9. Sofia mowed the lawn 2 times in May and 3 times in June. She was paid $5.00 each time she mowed. How much money did Sofia earn altogether?

Ⓐ $30

Ⓑ $15

Ⓒ $25

10. Donald bought some new clothes at a sale. He found a shirt for $6.98, socks for $1.29, and pants for $4.55. If tax was included in the price, about how much did Donald spend altogether?

Ⓐ $9.00

Ⓑ $13.00

Ⓒ $10.00

11. Jessie went to the store to get 1 gallon of milk, 3 pounds of string beans, and 1 pound of butter. She brought $6.00 with her. The milk costs $3.15 a gallon, the beans $0.46 a pound, and the butter $1.23 a pound. Does Jessie have enough money?

Ⓐ No, she needs $0.76 more.

Ⓑ Yes, she has $0.24 extra.

Ⓒ Yes, she has $1.16 extra.

12. Which of these means seven dollars and fifty-six cents?

Ⓐ $7.506

Ⓑ $75.06

Ⓒ $7.56

Counting Coins

DIRECTIONS

Write the amount in dollars and cents for each set of coins and bills.

1.

$ _____

2.

$ _____

3.

$ _____

4.

$ _____

5.

$ _____

6.

$ _____

Pockets Full of Change

DIRECTIONS

Compare each pocket of change.
Write **>**, **<**, or **=** between each set of pockets.

1.

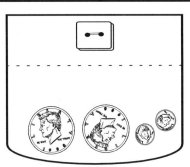 _____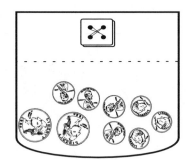

2.

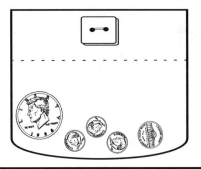 _____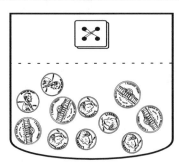

3.

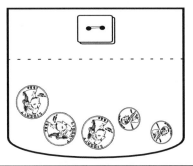 _____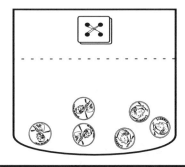

4.

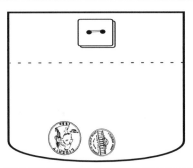 _____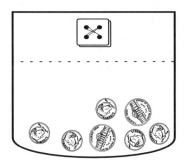

Computations with Money

DIRECTIONS
Find the quotient for each example.

1. $2.97 ÷ 3 = _____   **2.** $8.50 ÷ 5 = _____   **3.** $8.16 ÷ 4 = _____

4. $5.22 ÷ 6 = _____   **5.** $6.32 ÷ 8 = _____   **6.** $6.00 ÷ 5 = _____

DIRECTION
Estimate by rounding to the next higher dollar. Then find the product.

7. $6.38 → $7.00
         x   3 → x   3

9. $15.76 →
         x   4 →

8. $0.72 →
         x   9 →

10. $5.29
          x   6 →

DIRECTIONS
Write the number sentence and solve.

11. A bakery buys 6 baskets of apples. Each basket costs $9.40. What is the total cost of the apples?

_____

Name _____ Date _____

Baby Bucks

DIRECTIONS

Anna and Megan work for a baby-sitting service. They keep careful records of how many hours they baby-sit each week. Add the total hours for each week. Complete the time sheet.

Name _____ Anna Garcia
Month _____ July
Hourly pay _____ $2.57

Hours Worked

Week	Mon.	Tues.	Wed.	Thurs.	Fri.	Total Hours
1–5	3	7	5	4	2	
8–12	2	5	6	7	2	
15–19	1	3	5	2	3	
22–26	5	7.5	5.5	8	6	
29–31	3	5	4			

Total hours _____ for July

Name _____ Megan Hoffer
Month _____ July
Hourly pay _____ $2.41

Hours Worked

Week	Mon.	Tues.	Wed.	Thurs.	Fri.	Total Hours
1–5	4	5	2	3	5	
8–12	3	3	2	2	1	
15–19	3	7	6	4.5	6.5	
22–26	2	5	6	3	4	
29–31	2	5	5			

Total hours _____ for July

DIRECTIONS

Use the time sheet to solve. Round to the largest number.

1. Estimate how much Anna earned during the weeks of July 8 to 12 and July 15 to 19. During which week did she earn more? How much more?

_____

2. Estimate how much Megan earned during the weeks of July 8 to 12 and July 15 to 19. During which week did she earn more? How much more?

_____

3. During which week did Anna and Megan work the same number of hours? Estimate how much money each of them earned during that week.

_____

4. Estimate how much Anna earned in July. Estimate how much Megan earned in July. Estimate how many more hours Megan needed to earn as much as Anna.

_____

Money-Makers

Jack, Dave, Lisa, and Angie decided to earn some money. They set up a yard-care service. Two workers mowed lawns. The other two workers raked and weeded. They charged $5.00 an hour for their work. The 4 workers divided their money equally.

1. Mr. Kerbis hired the workers. He said he had a 3-hour job. He told them he would pay them $10.00. Was his offer reasonable? Was it too high or too low?

_____

2. What should Mr. Kerbis have paid? _____

3. Ms. Arnold hired the workers. The 4 workers spent 5 hours caring for her lawn. Ms. Arnold wanted to pay them $40.00. Was this reasonable? Was her offer too high or too low? _____

4. What should Ms. Arnold have paid the workers? _____

5. Mr. Maier hired them for a 4-hour job. He wanted to give them a tip. He thought the job should cost 5 times the tip. He planned a $2.50 tip. Was his planned tip reasonable? Was it too high or too low? _____

6. What should the tip have been? _____

7. The workers made $32.00 one day. They divided the money equally. Angie figured she would get $5.00. Was her estimate reasonable? Was it too high or too low?

_____

8. What should each worker's share have been? _____

Name _____ Date _____

Money for Music

DIRECTIONS
Choose the strategy and solve.

1. Ilya wants to buy a radio. Each week she saves $\frac{65}{100}$ of her $1.00 allowance. How much does Ilya save each week?

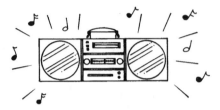

_____

2. The radio Ilya wants to buy costs $11.99. She helps her neighbor rake leaves and earns $8.25. How much more money does Ilya need to buy the radio?

_____

3. Ilya earned $8.25 and has saved her allowance for 8 weeks. How much money does Ilya have? (Hint: Read Exercise 1.)

_____

4. If the radio costs $11.99 and there is $0.83 tax, how much money does Ilya have left over?

_____

5. Ilya wants to buy some CDs. She begins to save her allowance again. She has 2 quarters, 4 dimes, 2 nickels, and 8 pennies. Write a number sentence using decimals to show how much money Ilya has.

_____

Name _____   Date _____

In the News

DIRECTIONS

Look through the sales section of a newspaper. Find the ads in which people try to sell items. Find the most expensive item for sale. Then find the least expensive. Paste the ads here, or copy them.

Tools: newspaper, glue

Name _____ Date _____

How Much for a Meal?

DIRECTIONS

Think of your favorite home-cooked meal. With the help of an adult, write down all of the necessary ingredients to make the meal and take your list to the grocery store. Find the price of each item, and write it on your list. As you shop, compare prices to get the most for your money. When you have found all of the grocery items, add the prices to find the total cost of the meal. You may use a calculator.

Grocery List

Item   Price

_____

_____

_____

_____

_____

_____

_____

_____

_____

_____

_____

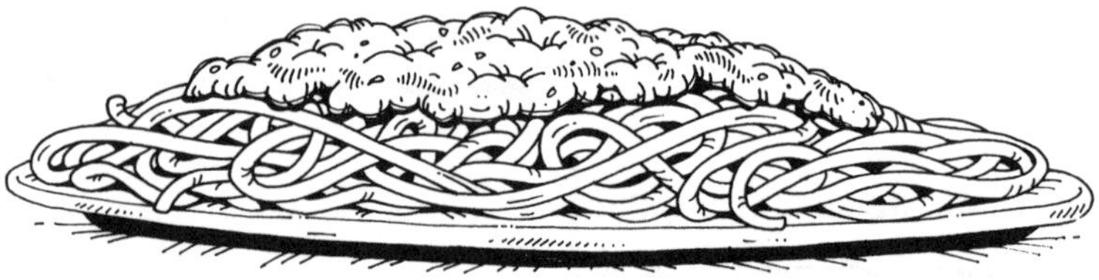

Tools: calculator

Name _____ Date _____

Unit 8 Assessment
Computation

DIRECTIONS
Read each problem and solve. Darken the circle for the correct answer.

1. What is the perimeter of this figure?

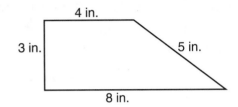

Ⓐ 15 in.
Ⓑ 20 in.
Ⓒ 20 ft

2. What is the perimeter of this figure?

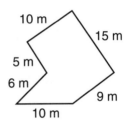

Ⓐ 41 m
Ⓑ 45 m
Ⓒ 55 m

3. What is the perimeter of this figure?

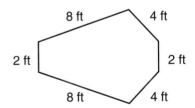

Ⓐ 28 ft
Ⓑ 24 ft
Ⓒ 28 in.

4. What is the area of this rectangle?

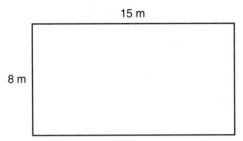

Ⓐ 120 sq m
Ⓑ 46 sq m
Ⓒ 130 sq m

5. What is the area of this picture frame?

Ⓐ 92 sq in.
Ⓑ 504 sq in.
Ⓒ 450 sq in.

6. What is the area of this figure?

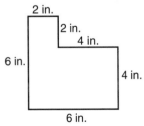

Ⓐ 40 sq in.
Ⓑ 24 sq in.
Ⓒ 28 sq in.

Go on to the next page

Unit 8 Assessment
Computation, p. 2

DIRECTIONS

Read each problem and solve. Darken the circle for the correct answer.

7. What is the volume of this cube?

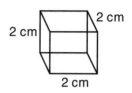

Ⓐ 8 cu cm

Ⓑ 6 cu cm

Ⓒ 4 cu cm

8. What is the volume of this box?

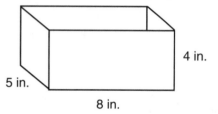

Ⓐ 17 cu in.

Ⓑ 52 cu in.

Ⓒ 160 cu in.

9. What is the volume of this aquarium?

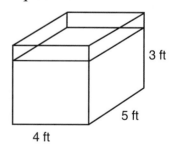

Ⓐ 75 cu ft

Ⓑ 60 cu ft

Ⓒ 12 cu ft

10. Jessica wants to put wallpaper border around the perimeter of her room. There are six walls that measure 10 ft, 12 ft, 15 ft, 8 ft, 5 ft, and 4 ft. How much wallpaper will she need?

Ⓐ 27 ft

Ⓑ 48 ft

Ⓒ 54 ft

11. Joe's aquarium is 30 cm wide, 60 cm long, and 30 cm deep. He has poured 23,000 cu cm of water into the tank. How much more water will he need to fill the tank?

Ⓐ 24,000 cu cm

Ⓑ 31,000 cu cm

Ⓒ 15,000 cu cm

12. Mr. Morais wants to put grass seed on his backyard. His backyard is 13 meters wide and 26 meters long. How many square meters of ground does he need to cover with seeds?

Ⓐ 338 sq meters

Ⓑ 78 sq meters

Ⓒ 260 sq meters

Estimate and Measure Perimeter

DIRECTIONS

The perimeter of a figure is the sum of the lengths of the sides. Choose 4 books. Estimate the perimeter of each in inches. Then find the perimeter using an inch ruler. Complete the table.

Book	Guess	Perimeter (in.)
1. Book 1		
2. Book 2		
3. Book 3		
4. Book 4		

DIRECTIONS

Estimate the perimeter of each figure in centimeters. Then find the perimeter using a centimeter ruler.

5.

estimate: _____

measure: _____

6.

estimate: _____

measure: _____

7.

estimate: _____

measure: _____

Tools: customary and metric rulers

Around the Outside

DIRECTIONS

The **perimeter** of a figure is the sum of the lengths of the sides. Estimate the perimeter for 1 and 2.

1.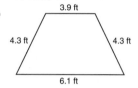

3.9 ft
4.3 ft   4.3 ft
6.1 ft

_____

2.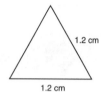

1.2 cm
1.2 cm

_____

DIRECTIONS

Find the perimeter for 3-8.

3.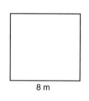

7 in.
4 in.   4 in.
7 in.

_____

4.

4 cm   4 cm
3 cm

_____

5.

8 m

_____

6.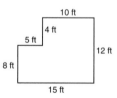

10 ft
4 ft
5 ft
8 ft   12 ft
15 ft

_____

7.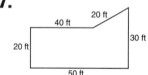

20 ft
40 ft
20 ft   30 ft
50 ft

_____

8.

10 m
15 m
5 m
6 m
10 m   9 m

_____

DIRECTIONS

Solve this problem.

9. Dana's yard is a rectangle that is 25 feet wide and 53 feet long. How many feet of fence will he need to go around his entire yard? _____

Name _____   Date _____

Finding Area

Area is the total space inside a plane figure. Area is stated in square units. Find the area of each figure. Label your answer in square units.

1.

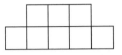

_____

2.

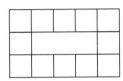

_____

3.

_____

4.

_____

5.

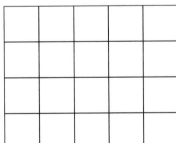

_____

6.

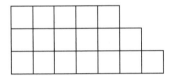

_____

Fill in squares with your pencil. Make three shapes, each with an area of 6 square units.

7.

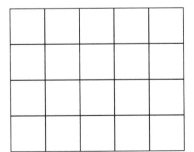

8.

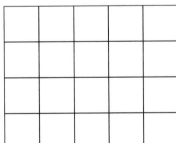

9.

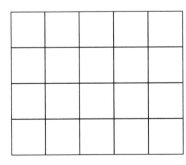

Name _____ Date _____

Finding Area: Rectangles

DIRECTIONS

Area is the total space inside a plane figure. Use this formula to find the area of a rectangle or square: Area = length X width, or A = l X w. Find the area.

1.

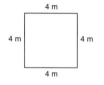

4 m

4 m   4 m

4 m

_____

2.

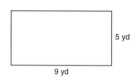

5 yd

9 yd

_____

3.

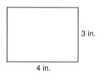

3 in.

4 in.

_____

4.

1 m

7 m

_____

5.

4 ft

4 ft

_____

6.

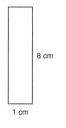

8 cm

1 cm

_____

7.

9 m

_____

8.

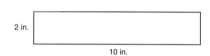

2 in.

10 in.

_____

9. l = 8 ft, w = 4 ft _____   **10.** l = 9 m, w = 11 m _____

11. l = 94 ft, w = 10 ft _____   **12.** l = 5 cm, w = 6 cm _____

Name _____ Date _____

Finding Area: Irregular Shapes

To find the area of irregular shapes, divide the figure into rectangles and squares. Find the area of each. Then add the areas of all the shapes together. Look at the picture. Answer the questions.

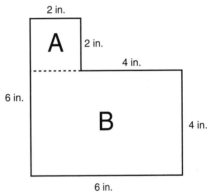

1. Find the area of part A. _____

2. Find the area of part B. _____

3. Add the areas of parts

A and B together. _____

Find the areas.

4.

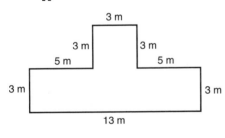

_____

5.

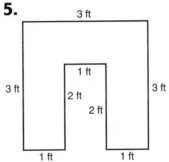

_____

6.

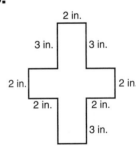

_____

Solve this problem.

7. This is a picture of the floor of Tanya's room. How many square feet of carpet will she need to cover her floor?

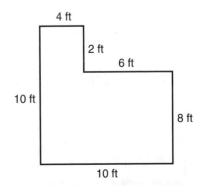

_____

Name _____ Date _____

Finding Volume Using Cubes

1.

_____

2.

_____

3.

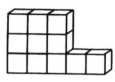

_____

4.

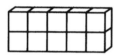

_____

5.

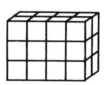

_____

6.

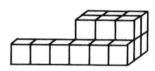

_____

7.

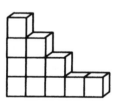

_____

8.

_____

9.

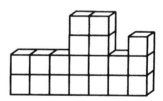

_____

10. Use centimeter cubes to duplicate the shapes in 1–9. The number of cubes you use should match the volume you found for each shape.

Tools: metric cubes

Name _____   Date _____

Boxed In

DIRECTIONS

Volume = length X width X height. Use this formula to find the volume of each.

1.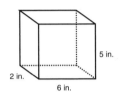
5 in.
2 in.
6 in.

_____

2.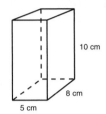
10 cm
8 cm
5 cm

_____

3.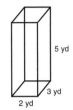
5 yd
3 yd
2 yd

_____

4.
2 ft
5 ft
4 ft

_____

5.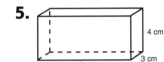
4 cm
9 cm
3 cm

_____

6.
2 mm
2 mm
16 mm

_____

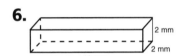

DIRECTIONS

Complete this table for rectangular prisms.

	Length	Width	Height	Volume
7.	2 cm	4 cm	8 cm	
8.	3 cm	5 cm	2 cm	
9.	8 cm	3 cm	1 cm	
10.	4 cm		2 cm	24 cubic cm
11.		4 cm	4 cm	96 cubic cm

DIRECTIONS

Write the number sentence and solve.

12. Ronald is filling his fish tank. The tank measures 13 inches by 9 inches by 9 inches. What is the volume of water the tank will hold?

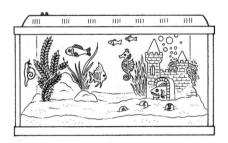

_____

Name _____ Date _____

Dream House

An architect designs homes on paper. If you were an architect, what kind of home would you design? You must include areas for preparing food, for eating, for sleeping, and for playing. Add walls, windows, doors, and furniture. Let each square below = 1 foot square. Figure the perimeter and the area of each room.

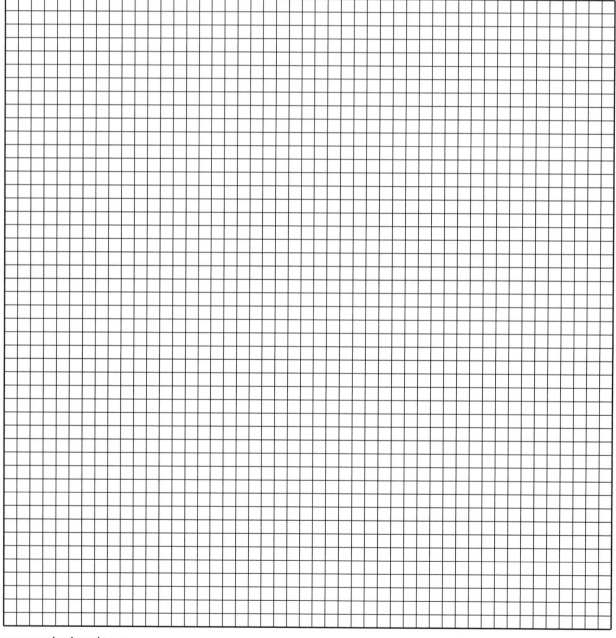

Be a Problem Solver

DIRECTIONS

Use the table below to answer questions 1-3.

Area of Largest States	
State	Area (in square miles)
Alaska	591,004
California	158,706
Montana	147,046
New Mexico	121,593
Texas	266,807

1. Which state has an area greater than that of Texas?

_____

2. Which state has about twice the area of New Mexico?

_____

3. Which state has the smallest area?

_____

4. What is the volume of a cube that is 10 cm by 10 cm?

_____

5. Jeremy has a box that is 2 feet long, 3 feet high, and 4 feet wide. What is the volume of the box?

_____

Go on to the next page.

Be a Problem Solver, p. 2

DIRECTIONS
Read each problem and solve.

6. Mrs. Weisman's chalkboard is 3 feet tall and 6 feet long. What is the area of the chalkboard in square feet?

_____

7. James is looking at a problem in his math book. There is a square that is 10 cm by 10 cm. It is divided into square centimeters. Half of the squares are shaded. What is the area in square cm that is not shaded?

_____

8. Manchu makes some 1-inch cube blocks as a present for his little sister. He finds a box that is 2 inches tall, 4 inches wide, and 12 inches long. Will all 100 blocks fit in the box?

_____

9. Daria's flower shop garden is an irregular shape with 6 sides. The sides are 10 meters, 15 meters, 9 meters, 10 meters, 6 meters, and 5 meters. How many meters of wire fencing will Daria need to buy to enclose her entire garden?

_____

10. Daria wants to buy fertilizer for a section of her garden that is 5 meters by 7 meters. The fertilizer bag says that she should use 1 pound per square meter. How many pounds of fertilizer should Daria buy?

_____

Measurement: Grade 4

Answer Key

Pp. 9–12 Overall Assessment

1. B	17. A
2. C	18. B
3. C	19. C
4. B	20. B
5. B	21. A
6. B	22. B
7. C	23. C
8. C	24. C
9. B	25. B
10. B	26. A
11. C	27. C
12. B	28. C
13. C	29. B
14. A	30. A
15. C	31. A
16. C	32. A

Pp. 13–14
Unit 1 Assessment

1. A	7. A
2. C	8. B
3. A	9. C
4. C	10. A
5. B	11. A
6. B	12. C

Pp. 15–16

1. minutes	13. meters
2. inches	14. kilograms
3. gallons	15. meters
4. feet	16. milligrams
5. minutes	17. milliliters
6. miles	18. centimeters
7. cups	19. kilograms
8. ounces	20. kilometers
9. feet	21. liters
10. tons	22. milligrams
11. ounces	23. meters
12. pints	24. kiloliters

P. 17

Students' answers will vary. Check for reasonable data.

P. 18

Students' answers will vary. Check for reasonable data.

P. 19

Students' graphs will vary. Check for reasonable data and steady climb of graph.

P. 20
1. about 60 minutes, or 1 hour
2. about 40 degrees
3. about $77.00
4. about 5 pounds
5. about 9 or 10 miles
6. about 8 quarts

Pp. 21–22
Unit 2 Assessment

1. C	7. C
2. A	8. B
3. B	9. B
4. B	10. A
5. A	11. C
6. A	12. B

P. 23

G shows $4\frac{5}{8}$ inches.
A. $\frac{1}{4}$ inch   F. $5\frac{1}{2}$ inches
B. $1\frac{3}{8}$ inches   1. $1\frac{13}{16}$ inches
C. $1\frac{3}{4}$ inches   2. $1\frac{11}{16}$ inches
D. $3\frac{1}{4}$ inches   3. $1\frac{15}{16}$ inches
E. $4\frac{5}{16}$ inches

P. 24
1. inches   5. 3 yd
2. feet   6. 16 ft
3. yards   7. 23 mi
4. feet   8. 400 yd

9. Mississippi
10. 1,040 miles
11. Bruster; Going through Bruster, it is 330 miles to Clear Valley. Going through Capital City, it is 398 miles to Clear Valley.

P. 25
1. a   7. centimeter
2. b   8. 5 dm
3. a   9. 10 m
4. decimeter   10. 16 km
5. meter   11. 2 m
6. kilometer

12. $7 \times 7 = 49$ km

P. 26
1–7. Students' answers will vary. Check charts for reasonable data.
8. Students should draw 3 inch by 3 centimeter rectangle.
9. No. She has only 90 inches of wood.
10. She would need more centimeters of wood because centimeters are shorter than inches.

P. 27

Students' answers will vary due to estimation. Accept any reasonable estimate.
1. 2,500–2,750 ft
2. Ruby Lane, Scarlet Road, Rouge Place
3. 1,000–1,250 ft
4. 3,250–3,500 ft

P. 28

1. C	4. B
2. A	5. C
3. C	6. A

P. 29
1. 52 mph
2. 4 mph; 3 mph
3. Tuesday
4. 10 miles

P. 30
1. 3,915 miles
2. 20,000 + 3,000 + 500 + 70 + 2
3. 2,348 > 2,315
4. 924 meters
5. 4,200 miles

P. 31
1. 4 yards
2. No. His ladder will only be 6 meters long unfolded.
3. Yes, exactly.
4. 8,837 feet
5. $1\frac{1}{8}$ miles
6. about 650 miles

P. 32

Students' answers will vary according to where they live.

Pp. 33–34
Unit 3 Assessment

1. C	7. B
2. B	8. A
3. C	9. B
4. A	10. B
5. C	11. C
6. B	12. A

P. 35
1. gallon (or quart)
2. cup
3. gallon
4. quart
5. teaspoon
6. pint
7. 2 tbsp
8. 4 pt
9. 10 gal
10. Ellie uses 4 cups of oatmeal to make cookies.
11. Regan pours a cup (or pint) of milk in his glass.
12. 2 pints

P. 36
1. liters   6. 500 mL
2. milliliters   7. 120 mL
3. liters   8. C
4. milliliters   9. B
5. 1 mL   10. B

11. The tall vase holds 2,000 mL of water. The wide vase holds more.

P. 37

Students' answers will vary. Check charts for reasonable data.

P. 38
1. October 28
2. September
3. Between the 21st and the 28th of October
4. September 20th and October 21st
5. $89.95

P. 39
1. 8 gal, 3 qt, 1 pt
2. Stone River; 6 gal, 1 qt
3. Pecos River; 9 gal
4. 2 gal, 2 qt, 1 pt
5. Indian River, Stone River or Blue River, Pecos River
6. 30 gal, 2 qt

P. 40
1. 1 gallon
2. $\frac{1}{24}$ of a cup
3. 37 quarts, or 9 gallons and 1 quart
4. 1 gallon, 3 quarts, and 1 cup
5. about 2 liters
6. 14 pints

P. 41
1. Creamy Punch
2. Fruity Cooler
3. Creamy Punch: 3-oz envelope; 2 c sugar; 4 c milk; 2 qt sherbet; 7 c soda water. Fruity Cooler: 3-oz envelope; $1\frac{1}{2}$ c sugar; 8 c water; 1 c orange juice; $\frac{1}{2}$ c lemon juice; 3 c pineapple juice.
4. Creamy Punch: 12–16 glasses; Fruity Cooler: 8–12 servings.

P. 42

Students' answers will vary.

Pp. 43–44
Unit 4 Assessment

1. C	7. B
2. A	8. C
3. C	9. B
4. B	10. A
5. A	11. C
6. B	12. B

Pp. 45–46
1. 54° F
2. 87° F
3. 41° F
4–9. Check students' work for accuracy.
10. −10° C
11. −20° C
12. 18° C
13–18. Check students' work for accuracy.

P. 47
1. 40° F
2. March and December or June and October
3. July
4. Between February and March
5. 5° F, increased to 20° F
6. about 83° F, 15° F

P. 48

Check students' work for accuracy in graphing numbers.
1. Between October and November
2. By 6° F
3. a decrease
4. December and February
5. 78° F
6. October

P. 49
1. 1st
2. 25th and 27th
3. Any day over 25°C; 13th, 14th, 15th, 16th, 18th, 21st, 22nd, 23rd, 24th, 25th, 26th, 27th, 28th, 29th, 30th, 31st
4. 5th
5. Check students' work for reasonable temperature recordings.

P. 50
1. 72° F
2. Gerard should plan another type of activity because 13° C is rather cold for swimming.
3. The 98° C pot is closer.
4. Yes. 76° F
5. The 33° F tray is closer.

Pp. 51–52
Unit 5 Assessment
1. B   7. C
2. A   8. B
3. C   9. A
4. B   10. B
5. A   11. C
6. A   12. C

P. 53
1. ounce   7. 1 lb
2. ounce   8. 7 lb
3. pound   9. 5 oz
4. ton   10. 80
   (or pound) 11. 26,000
5. pound   12. 4
6. ounce   13. 3 pounds

P. 54
1. grams   6. kilograms
2. grams   7. 1 g
3. kilograms   8. 1,750 kg
4. kilograms   9. 20 g
5. grams   10. 450 kg

11. 1,000 − 275 = 725 grams

P. 55
1. 176   4. 63
2. 100   5. 77
3. 52   6. 144

7. beaver, raccoon, fox, woodchuck, skunk, rabbit
8. The numbers are much smaller.

P. 56
Students' answers will vary. Check work for reasonable data.

P. 57
1. 137 g   5. 2,462 mg
2. 1,570 g   6. 30 mg
3. 25 kg   7. 11,000 g
4. 45 kg   8. 40 kg

P. 58

Winner	Prizes	Total oz	Cost of first oz	Cost of added ounces	Total mailing cost
Jane	CD and T-shirt	11 oz	9¢	70¢	79¢
Ralph	Game	9 oz	9¢	56¢	65¢
Maria	Mug	5 oz	9¢	28¢	37¢
Lin	T-shirt and mug	8 oz	9¢	49¢	58¢
Claus	CD and mug	13 oz	9¢	84¢	93¢

P. 59
1. A   4. A
2. C   5. B
3. B

P. 60
1. 40 pounds
2. 280 pounds
3. 20 pounds
4. Ms. Somner's
5. 40 pounds
6. 90 pounds

P. 61
1. 9 pounds
2. 15 pounds
3. 17 kilograms
4. 12 pounds
5. 600 grams
6. 62 pounds

P. 62
The least expensive way for Rita to mail her packages is to combine them. Their total weight will be 39 pounds, and the price will be $9.00.

Pp. 63–64
Unit 6 Assessment
1. C   7. A
2. C   8. C
3. B   9. B
4. A   10. B
5. B   11. A
6. A   12. A

P. 65
1. months   5. A
2. minutes   6. C
3. minutes   7. about 4:00
4. second

P. 66
1. 7:30, seven thirty, or 30 minutes past seven
2. 3:15, three fifteen, or fifteen minutes past three
3. 3:50, three fifty, or ten minutes till four
4. 12:30, twelve thirty, or thirty minutes past twelve
5–6. Lines go straight across.
7. Jason prepared the bread dough.

P. 67
1. 13½ hours
2. 10 hours, 5 minutes
3. 35 minutes
4. 5 hours
5. 7:45 A.M.
6. 35 minutes

P. 68
1. 4 more
2. 38 minutes
3. 22 minutes
4. Hound Dog Jones; 4 min

P. 69
1. 3 days
2. 2:00, Sunday
3. 6-8 year-olds
4. Sunday, 1:00

5. 3 hours
6. Baby contest and Judging of 4-H livestock projects

P. 70
Students' answers will vary. Check charts for reasonable data.

P. 71
Students' answers will vary. Check work for reasonable timetables.

P. 72
Students' answers will vary.

Pp. 73–74
Unit 7 Assessment
1. B   7. C
2. A   8. A
3. C   9. C
4. A   10. B
5. C   11. B
6. B   12. C

P. 75
1. $3.27   4. $1.20
2. $1.01   5. $1.00
3. $3.82   6. $0.79

P. 76
1. >   3. <
2. >   4. >

P. 77
1. $0.99   7. $21.00
2. $1.70   8. $9.00
3. $2.04   9. $64.00
4. $0.87   10. $36.00
5. $0.79   11. $56.40
6. $1.20

P. 78
Anna Garcia: 21, 22, 14, 32, 12, Total = 101
Megan Hoffer: 19, 11, 27, 20, 12, Total = 89
1. July 8 to 12; $30.00 more
2. July 15 to 19; $40.00 more
3. July 29-31; Anna earned about $40.00; Megan about $20.00
4. Anna: $300; Megan: $180; about 60 hours

P. 79
1. too low   5. too low
2. $15.00   6. $4.00
3. too high   7. too low
4. $25.00   8. $8.00

P. 80
1. $0.65   3. $13.45
2. $3.74   4. $0.63

5. .50 + .40 + .10 + .08 = $1.08

P. 81
Students' selections will vary. Check for reasonable choices.

P. 82
Students' results will vary. Check work.

Pp. 83–84
Unit 8 Assessment
1. B   7. A
2. B   8. C
3. A   9. B
4. A   10. C
5. B   11. B
6. C   12. A

P. 85
1–4. Students' answers will vary.
5. 12 cm
6. 12 cm
7. 8 cm

P. 86
1. 18 ft   6. 54 ft
2. 3 cm   7. 160 ft
3. 22 in.   8. 55 m
4. 11 cm   9. 156 ft
5. 32 m

P. 87
1. 8 sq units
2. 12 sq units
3. 6 sq units
4. 16 sq units
5. 15 sq units
6. 18 sq units
7–9. Students' shapes may vary. Check work.

P. 88
1. 16 sq m   7. 81 sq m
2. 45 sq yd   8. 20 sq in.
3. 12 sq in.   9. 32 sq ft
4. 7 sq m   10. 99 sq m
5. 16 sq ft   11. 940 sq ft
6. 8 sq cm   12. 30 sq cm

P. 89
1. 4 sq in.   5. 7 sq ft
2. 24 sq in.   6. 24 sq in.
3. 28 sq in.   7. 88 sq ft
4. 48 sq m

P. 90
1. 8 cu units   6. 18 cu units
2. 12 cu units   7. 11 cu units
3. 11 cu units   8. 3 cu units
4. 10 cu units   9. 19 cu units
5. 24 cu units

P. 91
1. 60 cu in.   7. 64 cu cm
2. 400 cu cm   8. 30 cu cm
3. 30 cu yd   9. 24 cu cm
4. 40 cu ft   10. 3 cm
5. 108 cu cm   11. 6 cm
6. 64 cu mm   12. 1,053 cu in.

P. 92
Students' plans will vary. Check work for perimeters and areas.

Pp. 93–94
1. Alaska
2. Texas
3. New Mexico
4. 1,000 cubic cm
5. 24 cubic feet
6. 18 sq ft
7. 50 sq cm
8. No.
9. 55 meters
10. 35 pounds